KT-371-717

ENGLISH LOVE SONGS

ENGLISH LOVE SONGS

Stainer & Bell

First published in 1980
by
Stainer & Bell Ltd
ISBN 0 85249 583 8

CONTENTS

THE ELIZABETHAN AND JACOBEAN COURT

CHARLES I, CAVALIERS AND THE RESTORATION COURT

GEORGIAN THEATRE, PUBLIC GARDEN AND CONCERT ROOM

THE VICTORIAN AND EDWARDIAN DRAWING ROOM

THE RECITAL ROOM

ACKNOWLEDGEMENTS

The publishers are grateful to the following for their ready cooperation in the preparation of this anthology:

The Musica Britannica Trust
The Executors of the late Thurston Dart
The Frank Bridge Trust
The Delius Trust
The John Ireland Trust

and to the following for permission to reproduce illustrations in their care:

The Art Gallery of Western Australia, p. 180
British Library, pp. 2, 7
British Museum, p. 11
Dulwich College Picture Gallery, p. 33
Munch Museet, Oslo, p. 196
National Portrait Gallery, pp. 10, 39, 49, 59, 88, 105, 111, 135, 142, 172, 209, 240
Royal College of Music, p. 166
University of London Library, p. 248
Victoria & Albert Museum, p. 183

Every effort has been made to trace all owners of copyright; if any have unwittingly remained undiscovered, the publishers offer apologies and will gladly make full acknowledgement in future editions.

The publishers also thank the following editors for agreeing to the inclusion of their editions:

Ian Spink, pp. 40, 43, 47, 48
Michael Pilkington, pp. 42, 50, 53, 81, 85, 86, 89, 92, 99, 102, 106, 109, 112, 115, 124, 126
Maureen Lehane and Peter Wishart, pp. 60, 65, 68, 72
Geoffrey Bush and Nicholas Temperley, pp. 136, 143, 147, 151, 156, 159, 163, 167, 173, 177

THE ELIZABETHAN AND JACOBEAN COURT

Setting words to music is as old as 'music'. Declaiming epic stories to an accompaniment formed part of the competitive festivals in classical Greece, as in many primitive peoples, whose music occupies the ethnomusicologists of today.

The early solo songs in Latin from the 7th century onwards include love songs and, throughout the Middle Ages, the poetry of love was essential to the profession of singing. Latin love songs gave way to French with the troubadours; the German and Austrian minnesingers sang love lyrics in their own language; the 'new art' of the 14th century was mainly French and Italian. The English, however, came slowly to the solo song. The first notable English songs were carols and the first notable English love songs were for voices with instruments 'in consort': we seem to have been shy about singing solos. Indeed, all the early love songs to be sung with a single instrument – the lute – were arrangements of chorus or consort songs in most European countries until the 17th century.

The exception was Spain, with the extraordinary songs of the *vihuelistas* who, in the space of 30 years in the middle of the 16th century, brought solo songwriting to Western ears. Perhaps they learnt from Arab song, which became for the 19th century a synonym for love-song . . . 'I'll sing thee songs of Araby'.

England had a tradition of songs with lute accompaniment as far back certainly as the reign of Henry VIII but they were mostly transcriptions of choral music until John Dowland published his *First Book of Ayres* in 1597. These were popular lyrics, many of them set to dance tunes with which Dowland had already had considerable success. The first song in this collection, 'If my complaints could passions move' began its musical life as 'Captain Digorie Piper's Galliard'. In his preface to 'the courteous Reader' the poet-composer tells how he had travelled for 16 years in France, Germany and Italy absorbing the lute music of great masters, after which he is now 'ready to practice at home'. The first three of the Dowland songs came from this 'first assays'. They were originally accompanied by lute and bass viol (playing the left hand of the piano part printed here).

All three of these songs were dedicated to Queen Elizabeth's Lord Chamberlain, Sir George Cary. The Elizabeth Court was by no means as in love with its Queen 'Gloriana' in 1597 as it had been in earlier years but it was in love with its new pleasure: the public theatre. As Lord Chamberlain, Cary was the censor of all plays and had his own company 'The Lord Chamberlain's Men' under the famous actor-manager Richard Burbage. Songs were featured in all these plays, though few have come down to us. It is interesting to compare the words Morley uses in 'It was a lover and his lass' with those printed in Shakespeare's *As You Like It* about a quarter of a century later: it seems that Shakespeare remembered most of them, but not quite all. But it is as well for us that Shakespeare used it, for the only surviving copy of Morley's *First Book of Ayres*, dated 1600, is in the Folger Shakespeare Library, Washington, DC – where it would certainly never have found its home but for the 'Shakespeare' song.

In Elizabethan and many Jacobean plays, female parts were played – and sung – by boys, so that even if the words to us seem to indicate a male singer no prima donna (of any standard) need feel self-conscious in performing these courtly songs.

The musical directors of the Whitefriars playhouse were Robert Jones and Philip Rosseter, both well-known Elizabethan and Jacobean courtiers alike. Both published *Books of Airs* in 1601 and both were royal lutenists to James I. Robert Jones chose to set words attributed to Sir Walter Raleigh in 'Now what is love?' Poor Sir Walter! Disillusioned with the Elizabethan court, his poetry betrayed his feelings only too well by 1601. He had little love left in him, yet he was to live 15 years after his imprisonment for conspiring against James I before he was mercifully beheaded. In its bitter sweet mood 'Now what is love?' is one of the most touching of English love songs.

Philip Rosseter was fortunate to have as his best friend Thomas Campian, possibly the finest song-writer of all during this period. In 'What then is love' – in contrast to Raleigh – Campian seems optimistic that his love will be returned with the jaunty refrain 'Come away, come away my darling'.

The tune of Ford's 'Since first I saw your face' has almost become an English folk song with its easy range and attractive sequences, whilst 'There is a lady sweet and kind' has become more known through its words, which have in turn attracted many later English composers. Thomas Ford is a shadowy figure. These two songs come from his collection of *Music of Sundry Kinds* published in 1607 and sold in St Dunstan's Churchyard, Fleet Street. St Dunstan's was the parish church of most lutenist song-writers in Jacobean times: Ford survived to become one of Charles I's musicians and died, having moved to Westminster, in 1648. 'Rest sweet nymphs' is another charmer for its poetry and lines such as 'whiles my lute the watch doth keep with pleasing sympathy'. Its writer, Francis Pilkington, was one of the few musicians working in the provinces (he was a chorister at Chester) to have his songs published in London.

These were the first genuinely 'solo' songs. The poetry makes it clear that 'Love' was still a god or goddess to worship in an artificial glance back at the Classical Age. Love could wound like Cupid; she was Venus the Goddess of Spring. Yet the English language itself had an earthly freshness at the time, expressing physical desire ('Sweet, stay awhile', 'Kiss me sweet'), almost innocent dalliance ('Sweet lovers love the Spring', 'Come away, come away my darling'), feigned despair ('She only drove me to despair when she unkind did prove') and real anguish ('I was more true to love than love to me').

English love songs of the early 17th century, despite the influence of continental masters in their technical expression, are musically matched, in tunes and turn of phrase, to the English language: the melody and harmony are as fresh as the lyrics . . . truly lyrical.

Sir Walter Raleigh: poet and courtier
?1552–1618

THE
FIRST BOOKE
of Songes or Ayres
of fowre partes with Tableture for the Lute:
So made that all the partes
together, or either of them seuerally may be song to the Lute,
Orpherian or Viol de gambo.
Composed by Iohn Dowland Lutenist and Batcheler of musicke in
both the Vniuersities.
Also an inuention by the sayd
Author for two to playe vpon one Lute.
Nec prosunt domino, quæ prosunt omnibus, artes.
¶ Printed by Peter Short, dwelling on
Bredstreet hill at the sign of the Starre, 1597

IF MY COMPLAINTS COULD PASSIONS MOVE

John Dowland

That my de - spairs had gov-ern'd me too long.
Thou made a god, and yet thy pow'r con - temn'd.
f
O Love, I live and die in thee,
That I do live, it is thy pow'r:
f
mf
Thy grief in my deep sighs still speaks:
That I de - sire it is thy worth:
mf
cresc.
Thy wounds do fresh - ly bleed in me,
If Love doth make men's lives too sour,
cresc.

p
mf
My heart for thy un-kind - ness breaks: Yet thou dost
Let me not love, nor live hence-forth: Die shall my
p
mf
dim.
hope when I de - spair, And when I
hopes, but not my faith, That you that
dim.
mf
hope, thou mak'st me hope in vain. Thou say'st thou canst my
of my fall may hear - ers be May here de - spair, which
mf
dim.
poco rit.
harms re - pair, Yet for re - dress, thou let'st me still com - plain.
tru - ly saith, I was more true to Love than Love to me.
dim.
poco rit.

LADY, IF YOU SO SPITE ME

John Dowland

that my heart op - press'd, oppress'd,
sure that my heart op-
cresc.
mf
-press'd, op-press'd and o - ver - cloy - ed, May break, may break
cresc.
mf
cresc.
f
thus o - ver - joy'd, o - ver - joy - ed.
cresc.
f
mf
If you seek to spill, to spill me,
mf

p
Come kiss me, sweet, come kiss me, sweet, come
mf
kiss me sweet, and kill me.
f
So shall your heart, your heart, your
heart be eas - ed,
dim.
And I shall rest content and
die, and die well pleas - ed.
cresc.

COME AWAY, COME SWEET LOVE

John Dowland

mf
souls in mu - tual bliss, Eyes were made for
-tain the stealth of love. Thi - ther, sweet love,
beau - ties but their own, Or - na-ment is
mf

dim.
p
beau - ty's grace, View - ing, rue - ing love's-long pain Pro-
let us hie, Fly - ing, dy - ing in de - sire Wing'd
nurse of pride, Plea - sure, mea - sure love's de - light. Haste
dim.

-cur'd by beau - ty's rude dis - - dain.
with sweet hopes and heav'n - ly fire.
then, sweet love, our wish - ed flight!

AWAKE SWEET LOVE, THOU ART RETURN'D

mf
dim.
On - ly her - self hath seem - ed fair: She on - ly I could
If she at last re - ward thy love, And all thy harms re -
cresc.
p
love, She on - ly drave me to de - spair, When she un - kind did
-pair, Thy hap - pi - ness will sweet - er prove, Rais'd up from deep de -
mf
dim.
prove. De-spair did make me wish to die; That I my joys might
-spair. And if that now thou wel - come be, When thou with her dost
cresc.
p
end: She on - ly, which, did make me fly, My state may now a - mend.
meet, She all this while but play'd with thee, To make thy joys more sweet.

SWEET STAY AWHILE

John Dowland

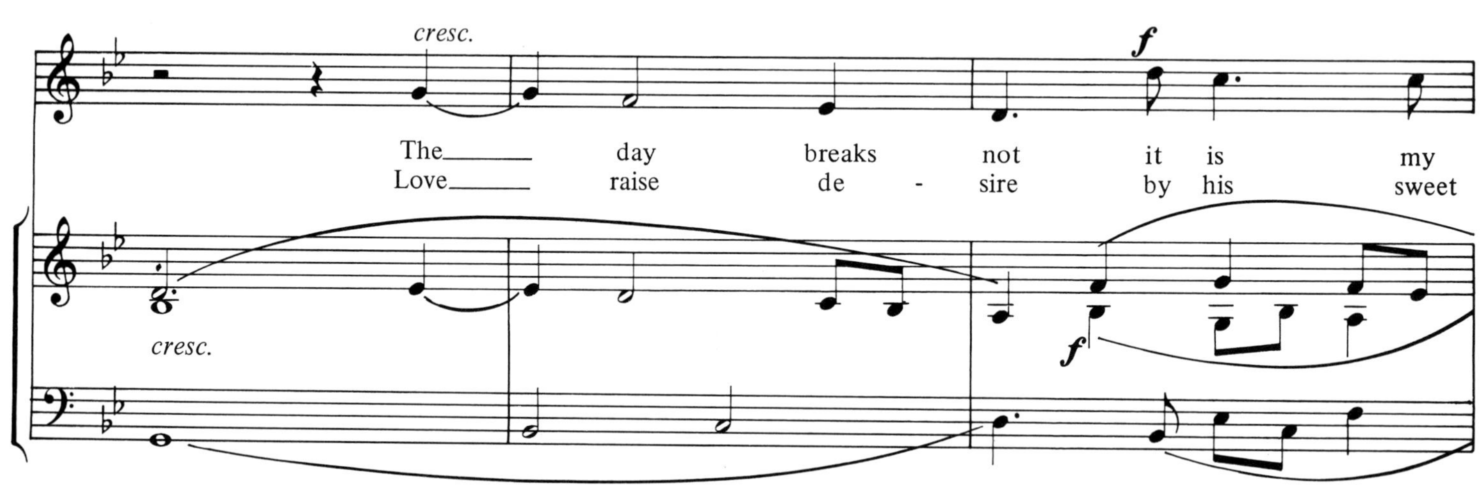

dim.
heart, To think that you and I must part.
charms With - in this cir - cle of thine arms:
dim.
p
f
O stay, O stay, or else my joys, my joys, my joys must die,
And let, and let, and let thy bliss - ful, bliss - ful kiss - es che - rish
dim.
p
dim.
p
And pe - rish in their in - fan - cy.
Mine in - fant joys, that else must pe - rish.

WHAT THEN IS LOVE BUT MOURNING

Attributed to Thomas Campian

Philip Rosseter

THERE IS A LADY SWEET AND KIND

Thomas Ford

NOW WHAT IS LOVE

Words attributed to
Sir Walter Raleigh

Robert Jones

★saunc*ing*: *sanctus*

LOVE IS A BABLE

Robert Jones

'Tis full of pas - sions Of sun - dry
An ar - rant li - ar, Fed by do -
A priv - y mis - chief, And such a
A mon - strous cheat - er, Ev - 'ry man's
fa - shions, 'Tis like, 'tis like, 'tis
- sire, It is, it is, it
sly thief, No man, no man, no
debt - or, Hang him, hang him, hang
dim.
like I can - not, I can - not, I can - not,
is, and yet it, and yet it, and yet it,
man knows which way, knows which way, knows which way,
him, and so let, and so let, and so let,
p
cresc.
'tis like, 'tis like I can - not tell what.
it is, it is, and yet it is not.
no man, no man knows which way to find.
hang him, hang him, and so let him go.

IT WAS A LOVER AND HIS LASS

Thomas Morley

birds do sing hey ding a ding a ding, hey ding a ding a ding, hey ding a ding a ding, Sweet
lo - vers love the Spring, in Spring - time,
in Spring - time, the
on - ly pret - ty ring time, When birds do sing hey ding a ding a ding, hey
ding a ding a ding, hey ding a ding a ding, Sweet lo - vers love the Spring.

SINCE FIRST I SAW YOUR FACE

Thomas Ford

The sun whose beams most glorious are
Rejecteth no beholder;
And your sweet beauty past compare
Made my poor eyes the bolder.
Where beauty moves and wit delights
And signs of kindness bind me,
There, O there, where'er I go,
I'll leave my heart behind me.

Richard Burbage: actor-manager of 'The Lord Chamberlain's Men'
?1567–1619

REST SWEET NYMPHS

Francis Pilkington

p
pleas - ing sym - pa - thies, Lul - la lul - la - by,
- sem - ble your true loves: Lul - la lul - la - by,
joy, and nev - er moan. Lul - la lul - la - by,
p
Lul - la lul - la - by, Sleep sweet - ly, Sleep
Lul - la lul - la - by Your kiss - es Your
Lul - la lul - la - by Hath pleas'd you And
sweet - ly, Let no - thing af - fright ye, In
bliss - es Send them by your wish - es, Al -
eas'd you, And sweet slum - ber seiz'd you, And
calm con - tent - ments lie.
- though they be not nigh.
now to bed I hie.

CHARLES I, CAVALIERS AND THE RESTORATION COURT

The lutenist songwriters usually wrote, played and sang their own songs. In the days of Charles I, composers turned to the courtly poets in the Campian tradition and the new playwrights such as Ben Jonson for their lyrics and they intended their songs to be sung in as many ways as were possible for professional and amateur singers. Instead of telling the accompanist exactly what to play, they wrote the words and tune then added a bass line with or without 'shorthand' numbers that told the accompanist what chords to use in filling in the harmony. This system known as 'figured bass' was used to accompany solo song for about 150 years and we must always remember that any performance of these songs now can only be in an 'edition' (or 'realisation' as it is sometimes called). The traditional ways of improvising an accompaniment over a figured bass were ignored by the editors and publishers who began to re-issue this music about 100 years ago; they simply re-harmonised the tunes in the style of their time, as Benjamin Britten did in his 'realisation' of Purcell. The songs printed here have all been edited by scholar-performers who have studied the books of the period in which people were taught to accompany, and represent at least an enlightened attempt to re-create their sounds on the piano. Singers would usually have been accompanied on the lute with a string bass until the last quarter of the 17th century when the harpsichord became the favourite instrument (sometimes with a cello amplifying the bass).

Finding copies of songs written during the reign of Charles I is not easy, since no song books seem to have been published after 1622 until the enterprising publisher John Playford marketed his first edition of *Select Musical Ayres and Dialogues* in 1652. The songs by those who were 'Musicians to the King' passed from hand to hand and were often changed as they were copied. Fortunately for us, three of the most famous composers wrote their songs in books which they kept, presumably hoping to have them published some time; and these autographed copies survive today in London (the Lawes brothers) and Oxford (John Wilson). Two other manuscripts, made by contemporary theatre musicians who probably copied them for performances, are now housed in New York Public Library and help to fill the publishing 'gap'.

Nicholas Lanier (1588–1666) was the first Master of the King's Music appointed by Charles I. His first songs appear in lutenist collections; one or two songs for plays are in the New York manuscript, but 'Though I am young' (written for Ben Jonson's *The Sad Shepherd* in 1640) first appears in the Playford 'Select Ayres' in 1652. He was highly regarded by poets, among them John Donne and Robert Herrick. The second 'part' follows an earlier tradition of the lutenists, making it possible to sing the song not only as a solo but also as a duet (with a loved one) or as an unaccompanied 'threesome' (with a rival singing the bass!).

'Take, O take those lips away' is a frank appreciation of physical charms not yet surrendered. John Fletcher may have been a collaborator in Shakespeare's plays and these words, set by John Wilson for a play called *The Bloody Brother* (acted as early as 1620) are a re-working from *Measure for Measure*. Wilson himself, who may well have acted in Shakespeare's company, was the King's favourite lutenist and, according to his Oxford Doctorate in 1645, he had become 'the most noted Musician of England'. He remained a Royalist in Oxfordshire throughout the Civil War, becoming Professor of Music at Oxford in 1656 (when he finished the autograph collection of his songs and presented them to the Bodleian Library there on condition that none should see them till after his death).

Henry Lawes and his younger brother, William were a redoubtable combination of songwriters for the theatre. Henry wrote over 350 songs and William may have had a hand in many of them, as the confusion of attributions in the late 17th-century publications suggests. Both did the music for Sir John Suckling's *Aglaure*, first performed in 1637. In this book Henry is represented by 'No, no, fair heretic' and William by 'Why so pale and wan, fond lover?'. Henry Lawes' song has the new, almost operatic beginning, typical of the stylised theatre then. He continues with – and brings back – the galliard dance tune (in triple time) from which much popular song had come. In both his songs, William keeps things simple, preferring to write a 'catchy' tune to a clever, over-dramatised version.

Suckling was a typical Cavalier – gallant, sensual and clear that the King stood for his way of life; Herrick liked women 'as he might like fruit or cakes'. Both of them esteemed Ben Jonson. As Herrick wrote:

> When I a verse shall make
> Know I have prayed thee,
> For old religion's sake,
> Saint Ben, to aid me.

The Cavalier poets may not have had the deep feeling of Elizabethans, but they were still clear and clean in their sensuality:

> Then be not coy, but use your time . . .
> For having lost but once your prime
> You may forever tarry.

Celia was the new goddess of love in the later 17th century. From Ben Jonson's 'Drink to me only' (dedicated 'to Celia') and 'Come, my Celia, let us prove, while we may, the Sports of Love' she was a new invention of poets to personify love:

> Wise poets, that wrapt Truth in tales,
> Know her themselves through all her veils.
> (Carew)

After the Restoration, she was still popular. Even John Blow, who was

Master of the Children at the Chapel Royal for over 30 years, and above all thought of as a church composer, could enjoy setting such a poem as 'Tell me no more' (addressed to Celia), which clearly finds 'laws of honour' irksome to anyone in love. In 'Of all the torments' Celia has become 'Sylvia' and once again the near operatic style is contrasted with a simple dance tune in triple time: the old popular dance – the Galliard – has given way to the 'Minuet'. Popular song followed popular dance.

The greatest of all Restoration composers – and arguably the greatest English songwriter of all – was Blow's own pupil, Henry Purcell.

In this selection, there is room for only four of Purcell's love songs. His views of love, like most Restoration songwriters brought up as choirboys, was sophisticated. He could enjoy vulgarity as his 'catches' (tunes in canon which gave us the word 'catchy' for a tune) show. Drink could at any time replace women who were there to be seduced, or if you married one, cursed:

'Tis women makes us love
'Tis love that makes us sad
'Tis sadness makes us drink
And drink makes us mad.

He could feign love ('What shall I do?' or 'I attempt from Love's sickness to fly'); become passionately ecstatic ('Sweeter than roses'); or be all-knowing, passion spent ('Ah, how sweet it is to love!'). All the four songs were written for plays between 1690 and 1695, performed in London's Dorset Gardens Theatre (off Fleet Street) or Drury Lane.

The lyrics for Restoration plays were often the work of several hands and Purcell overcame them all. 'What shall I do' comes from *Dioclesian* which had more music than dialogue and, in the alternative title *The Prophetess* was certainly heralding English opera. *The Prophetess* was concocted from an earlier John Fletcher play by the towering figure of the Restoration stage, Thomas Betterton, whose company occupied both the theatres for which Purcell wrote. *The Indian Queen*, for which Purcell wrote 'I attempt from love's sickness to fly' was John Dryden's first 'serious' verse musical, written in collaboration with his brother-in-law Sir Robert Howard (who actually contributed this number). Dryden became one of Purcell's greatest admirers and 'Ah, how sweet it is to love' was one of his favourite settings. On the death of 'Mr Purcell' he wrote

. . . The heavenly choir, who heard his notes from high,
Let down the scale of music from the sky;
They handed him along,
And all the way he taught, and all the way they sung . . .

Not, perhaps the best of verse; but a sincere tribute from the outstanding dramatist of Purcell's lifetime.

John Dryden: poet, dramatist and critic
1631–1700

A copy, dated 1698, of a portrait by the German born painter to the Court, Sir Godfrey Kneller. ?1646–1723

THOUGH I AM YOUNG

Ben Jonson

Nicholas Lanier

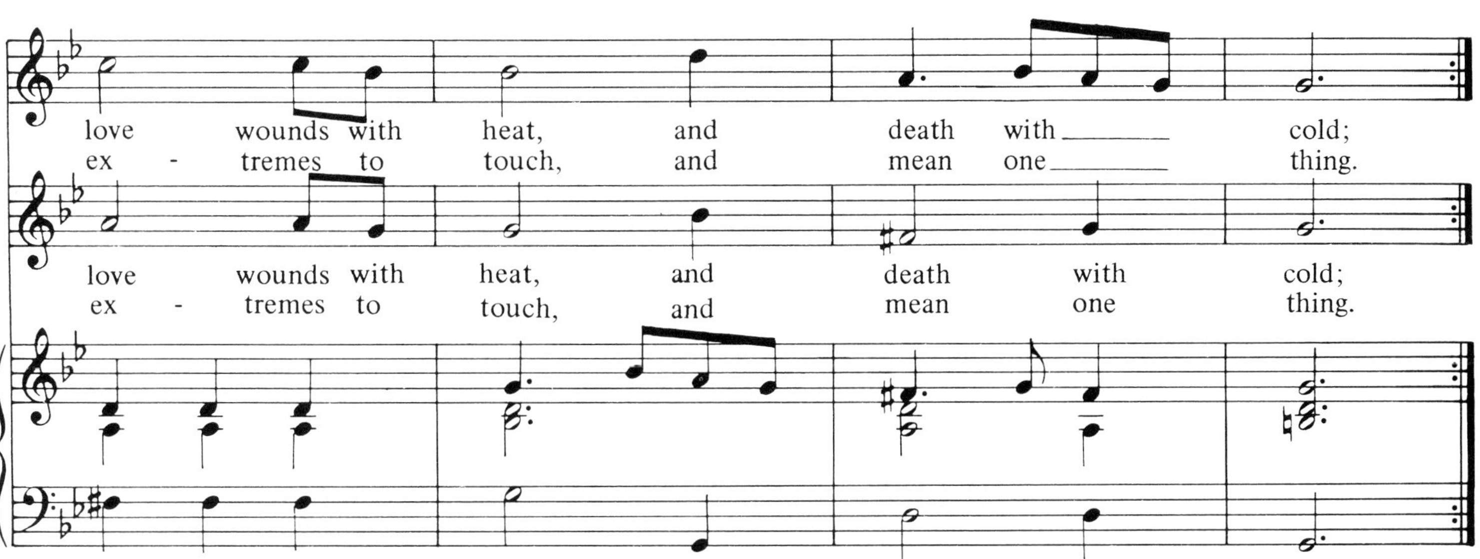

2. As in a ruin, we it call
One thing to be blown up, or fall;
Or to our end, like way may have,
By a flash of lightning, or a wave;
So love's inflamed shaft, or brand,
May kill as soon as death's cold hand;
Except love's fires the virtue have
To fright the frost out of the grave.

Repeat: 'May kill as soon' and 'To fright the frost' (verse 2).

TAKE O TAKE THOSE LIPS AWAY

William Shakespeare/John Fletcher

John Wilson

NO, NO, FAIR HERETIC

Sir John Suckling

Henry Lawes

More than I did the last, 'twould then so fall, I might not
love at all. Love that can flow, and can ad - mit in -
- crease, Ad - mits as well an ebb, and may grow
[𝅗𝅥 = 𝅗𝅥.]
3/4
tr

[♩. = 𝅗𝅥]
(♫ ♩.)
less. True love is still the same; The tor - rid zones
And those more fri - gid ones It must not know: For love grown_
cold or hot Is lust or friend - ship, not The thing we have, for

[𝅗𝅥 = 𝅗𝅥.]
that's a flame_ would_ die Held_ down, or_ up too_ high;
Then think I love more than I can ex - press, And
would_ love more, could I but love thee less.
tr

WHY SO PALE AND WAN, FOND LOVER?

Sir John Suckling

William Lawes

GATHER YOUR ROSEBUDS WHILST YOU MAY

Robert Herrick

William Lawes

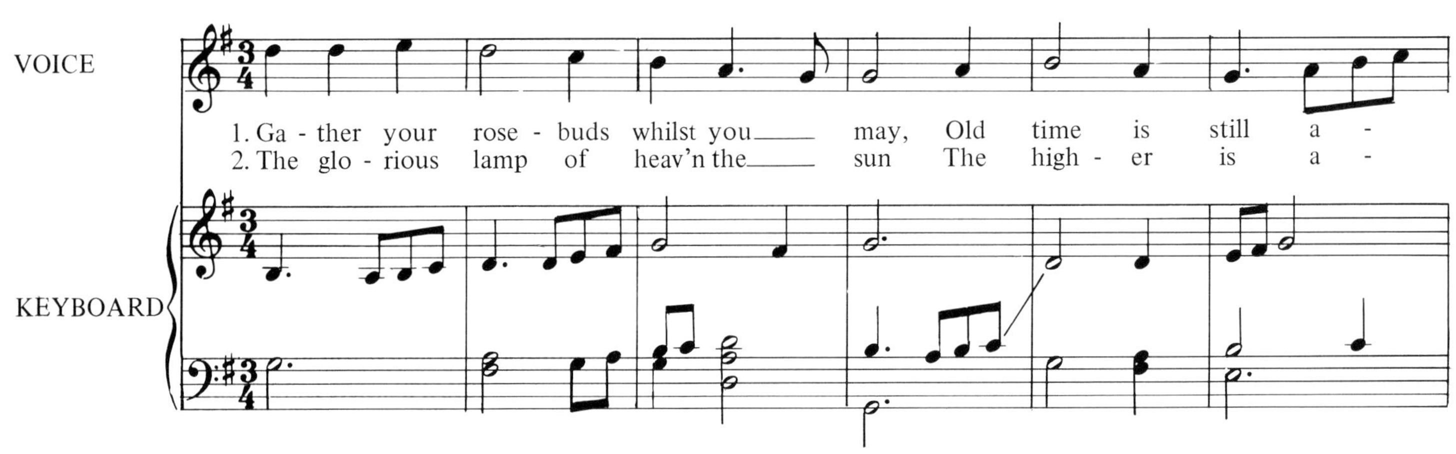

3. That fate is best that is the first
Whilst youth and blood are warmer;
But being fled, grows worse and worse,
And ill succeeds the former.

4. Then be not coy, but use your time
And whilst you may go marry:
For having lost but once your prime,
You may forever tarry.

John Blow: composer, organist and royal musician
1649–1708

This fine engraving by Robert White was used as a frontispiece to 'Amphion Anglicus', a collection of the composer's songs published by subscription in 1700 and dedicated to the Princess (afterwards Queen) Anne.

TELL ME NO MORE

John Blow

Notes The tempo should be fairly fast, but limited by the speed at which the slides in bars 33, 35 and 37 can be sung clearly. This rondo style was an import from Italy. The repetitions may be decorated if desired.

more, no more, you love. Can they pre - tend to love, who do re -
- fuse what love per - suades them to? Tell me no more, no
more you love. Who once has felt his ac - tive fire, dull
laws of ho - nour will dis - dain. Tell me no more, no
tr

more you love; in vain, fair Ce - lia you would be thought, you would be thought, you
would be thought his slave; and yet you will not, and yet you will not to his pow'r sub -
- mit. Tell me no more, no more you love; in vain, fair
Ce - lia, in vain, fair Ce - lia you this pas - sion feign.

OF ALL THE TORMENTS

John Blow

Notes An energetic and strongly accented *allegro* tempo for the first section will sustain interest through the repetitions; some echo effects might be used in several places. Decorations have been suggested in the ensuing minuet.

lives are curst, of all the tor - - - - - ments,
of all the tor - - - - - ments, all the
cares, Of all, all the plagues, of all, all the plagues, of all, all the
plagues a lo - - ver bears, Sure ri - - - - - -
7 6 6 4 5 3
7 6
4 3
♮3
♯3 7 6 ♮3 6 5 ♭5

★One note higher in the original.

grown; In love a-lone we hate to find, we hate to find Com-pa - nions of our
woe, in love a-lone we hate to find, we hate to find com-pa - - - - - - - - - - - - nions of our woe.
Syl - via, for all those pangs you see, for

tr
all those pangs, all, all those pangs you
6
7
6
6
4
♮3
tr
see, As la - bouring in my breast, I beg not that you'd
7
♮6
6
5
♮3
♮3
♮3
6
5
♮3
1
fa - vour me, But that you'd slight the rest.
2
rest. How great so e'er your ri - gours are, With

them a - lone I'll cope, I can en -
- dure, I can en - dure my own de - spair, But
not an - o - ther's hope; I can en - dure my
own de - spair, but not an - o - ther's hope.
7
4

Henry Purcell: The composer as a young man.
1659–1695

This picture, by Kneller (see page 49), was given by Purcell to one John Church, whose family owned it for almost 100 years. After passing through the hands of two more families, it was bought by the English musicologist William Barclay Squire and bequeathed to the National Portrait Gallery.

WHAT SHALL I DO TO SHOW HOW MUCH I LOVE HER?

Beaumont and Fletcher

Henry Purcell

Notes This song, perhaps almost more than any other in the present collection, repays reading, knowing and feeling the words: watch out for emphases in the poem, and then relate these to Purcell's setting. Colour the words: 'melt' with a long 'm'; 'implore' with lots of 'pl', and perhaps the section beginning 'Since gods' could be rather more conversational – more pointed – than languishing. The young man is surely not too melancholy about his love; in fact the lines beginning 'till for her own sake' are positively humorous.

move her, Those com - mon me - thods of love ___ she'll de -
- spise. I will love more than man e'er ___ lov'd ___ be -
- fore me; Gaze on her all the day, and ___ melt ___ all the
night; Till for her own sake, at

last she'll im - plore me To love her
less to pre - serve our de - light. Since gods them -
- selves could not e - ver be lov - - ing,
Men must have breath - ing re - cruits for new

joys; I wish my love could be
e - ver im - prov - - ing, Though ea - ger
love more than sor - row de - stroys.
In fair Au - re - lia's arms leave me ex -

-pir - ing, To be em - balm'd by the
sweets of her breath; To the last
mo - ment I'll still be de - sir - ing;
Ne - ver had he - ro so glo - rious a death.

AH! HOW SWEET IT IS TO LOVE

John Dryden

Henry Purcell

Notes The singer here is surely no longer young. The song is almost one long, rather sad sigh, but there's a smile there too. When you come to 'all, all', emphasise the off beat; it gives a sighing effect.

2
-sire! And what pleas - - ing pains, and what
pleas - - ing pains we prove, When first, when
first we feel a lov - er's fire; Pains of
love are sweet - - er far, Than all, all,

all, all, all, all o - ther plea - sures are;
Pains of love are sweet - - er far, Than
all, all, all, all o - ther plea - - -
- - - sures are. And what are.
1
2

I ATTEMPT FROM LOVE'S SICKNESS TO FLY

Sir Robert Howard

Henry Purcell

Notes The words are apparently serious, but the music belies this and it would not surprise us if the young man was not as passionately in love as he suggests, but indulging in a little seventeenth-century posturing; so do likewise. The essence of the song is elegance and if the odd affectation creeps in, let it.

pain; No more now, no more now fond heart with pride, no more swell, Thou can't not raise forces, thou can't not raise forces e - nough to re - bel. I at - tempt from love's sick - ness to

fly ______ in___ vain, Since I am my-

-self my own fe - ver, since I___ am___ my - self my___ own___

fe - ver___ and___ pain; For love has more___ pow'r, and less

mer - cy than fate, To make us___ seek___ ru - in, to___

make__ us__ seek__ ru - in, and__ love those__ that__ hate. I at -
-tempt__ from love's__ sick - ness to fly__ in__
vain,__ Since I am__ my - self__ my__ own__ fe - ver, since
I__ am__ my - self my__ own__ fe - ver__ and__ pain.

SWEETER THAN ROSES

Thomas Norton

Henry Purcell

Notes The problem here is to give the picture of utter ecstasy: you don't actually mention *what* is sweeter than roses until bar 16, which is surely a sign that you are in love. Within the discipline of the notes, the feeling must appear free and spontaneous, but the rhythm must remain. No such problems after 'Then shot like fire', and the final section is a shout of joy.

ro - ses, or cool, cool ev' - - - ning
breeze, On a warm flow - 'ry shore, Was the dear, the
piu mosso
dear, the dear, dear, dear kiss; First tremb -
mf
rall.
tempo primo
- ling, first tremb - ling made me, made me freeze,
etc.
etc.

allegro
made me freeze;
Then shot like fire all,
f
all,all, all o'er,
then shot like fire all, all, all, all, then shot like fire
Allegro
all, all o'er.
poco f
What ma-gic has vic - to -

- - - - - rious love,
What ma-gic has vic -
-to - - - - - - -
- - rious love, For all, all, all I touch, all,
p

all, all, all I touch or see; Since that dear,
dear kiss I hour-ly, hour-ly prove, All, all, all,
cresc.
all is love, all, all, all, all, all, all is love, all, all, all, all, all is love,
all, all, all, all, all is love, is love to me.

GEORGIAN THEATRE, PUBLIC GARDEN AND CONCERT ROOM

It is often thought that music in England died with Purcell and was only reborn with the music of Handel. This is not true of songwriting, which retained its direct and attractive setting of the English language. Throughout the 18th century, large audiences followed their favourite actors and singers in the London theatres. The songs they heard were repeated, as 'popular' favourites, in the public garden concerts and in the concert rooms of amateur, music-loving 'society'.

The major musical theatre for the first half of the century was Drury Lane; in the second half Covent Garden (the 'Opera' House) held sway. Throughout the whole time, public gardens received the theatre's music, passed it on in a different atmosphere and became the touchstone of popular musical fashion.

Daniel Purcell, younger brother of Henry, had helped to complete *The Indian Queen*. With the ruler of Drury Lane, Sir Richard Steele, he supplied music such as 'Let not love' for fashionable plays. The songs were then taken up in public concerts and became popular successes. The popularity of music in the theatre began to crowd out the plays themselves, which were shortened to accommodate 'the entertainment'. Star singers came from Italy; English rivals rose against them. English love songs remained direct, dance-like and attractive.

The Jacobean 'air' had become known as a 'Ballad' and ballad sheets circulated in all quarters of society during the 18th century. The coarseness of much Restoration comedy was somehow avoided in the simplicity and artlessness of the music, so that a song like 'Cupid, make your virgins tender' is quite persuasively acceptable.

George Monro adds to the praises of 'Celia' in a lovely, haunting tune as late as 1730. Monro, organist of St Peter's, Cornhill (the 'actors' church in the City of London) wrote many popular songs as part of his job as resident harpsichordist at the theatre in Goodman's Fields.

Public 'pleasure gardens' – the ancestors of 'Parks and Gardens' in English municipalities – were opened up in the grounds of former stately homes in the 17th century. The most popular in London was Spring Garden at Vauxhall (once within the estate of 'Fox Hall'). Tom Brown, a hack writer, in surveying *Amusements, Serious and Comical* in London, 1700, wrote of Spring Garden:

> In the close walks the most experienced masters have often lost themselves in looking for their daughters.

Samuel Pepys counted a visit amongst his favourite pastimes . . . and it is no wonder that singers of love songs were in demand. In 1730 the Garden acquired a new owner who installed an open-air concert hall for a full orchestra and built a rotunda for performances 'if wet'. Concerts on every evening began in 1736 and thousands of songs were written for first, and in many cases, last – performance there. Spring Garden had only three music directors in the next 100 years: Arne, Hook and Bishop.

Thomas Arne was the popular composer of Shakespeare settings for Drury Lane Theatre productions and also for the 'pantomimes' there. These pantomimes, weakling descendants of the Italian Commedia dell'Arte, included a 'Harlequinade' which usually needed at least one love song for Harlequin and Columbine. Such a song is 'O come, O come, my dearest': the lyrics by one 'Pritchard' are obviously by the hack hired for the pantomime, who may however have been related to a leading Drury Lane actress of the day, 'Mrs Pritchard'. The company was headed by Garrick and the most popular singing actress was Kitty Clive who sang Arne's song many times both in the theatre and in Spring Garden.

Arne had other 'resident' singers at Spring Garden. Thomas Lowe, a tenor from Drury Lane, appeared there for 20 years. He sang such pretty trifles as 'Jenny' who starts as a simple maid and then becomes Daphne pursued by Phoebus (Apollo). Musically, however, 'Jenny' is not so trifling as Arne parodies the Italianate oratorio semiquavers of Handel, only to return to the knowing minuet-like tune at the end.

'The fond Appeal' was written for Arne's mistress, Charlotte Brent, and seems more touched by a genuine passion. In 'The Timely Admonition' the moral is wrapped up once more in classical allusion, this time following the high fashion for tales of shepherds and swains set by Handel's 'Acis and Galatea' attributing the seduction to Virgil's shepherd Daman. As with all Handel's English songs, this is a 'Minuet-Song'.

William Boyce, Master of the King's Music, is in musical history books – like John Blow earlier – as a church musician. But at Drury Lane, he and Arne were always in each other's way . . . at least according to the contemporary reporter Charles Burney, who was Arne's apprentice both at Drury Lane and Spring Garden. Neither song here could be thought pious, but they are musically four-square and betray Boyce's main occupation in the organ loft. Although the Chloe of 'Tell me no more' is another Greek shepherdess in the words – which were written long before Boyce set them – the Master of the King's Music might have been accused of *lèse-majesté* since Alexander Pope in his *Moral Essays* – which were widely known – refers throughout to George II's mistress, Lady Suffolk, as 'Chloe': it was perhaps as well that the King's command of English was so poor.

James Hook, who succeeded Arne as resident composer at Spring Garden in 1774, published over 2,000 songs in annual songbooks during his lifetime. By this time, it was usual to provide an orchestral introduction – the Garden orchestra had flutes, horns, strings and organ or harpsichord – and a tailpiece (or short coda) in the manner of Italian and Viennese opera.

But in the Georgian concert rooms and houses the harpsichord alone provided enough accompaniment. All three songs by Hook in this book were written for the gardens which were re-named 'Vauxhall Gardens' in 1786. They are no longer 'Minuet-songs' but artfully simple 'arias'. The last, 'Take me, take me, some of you' betrays the changed attitude to explicit sex in the late 18th century, for Dryden originally wrote:

Young I am and yet unskilled
How to make a lover yield:
How to keep, and how to gain,
When to love; and when to feign.

Take me, take me, some of you,
While I yet am young and true;
Ere I can my soul disguise;
Heave my breasts, and roll my eyes.

Stay not till I learn the way,
How to lie, and how betray;
He that has me first, is blest,
For I may deceive the rest.

Could I find a blooming youth,
Full of love and full of truth,
Brisk, and of a jaunty mien
I should long to be *fifteen*.

The concert rooms of Bath and London were dominated for many years by the Linley family. Thomas Linley senior was the father-in-law of the play-wright Sheridan and, together with another partner, they took over Drury Lane Theatre from Garrick in 1776. 'When a tender maid' is a very proper product of their partnership.

Perhaps the finest unknown English songwriter of the last decade of the 18th century was Stephen Storace. He and his sister, the singer Nancy Storace, had been trained in Italy and moved to Vienna in Mozart's happiest days. When they returned to England, the standard of London's musical life was disillusioning and they settled with the Linleys in Bath. Thomas Linley enticed them both back to Drury Lane and 'How mistaken is the lover' comes from an adaptation of a Viennese opera, a re-working of an earlier piece. It owes not a little to *Così fan Tutte*, that most sophisticated of all love stories in song.

Although Italian opera had such an impact on London society in the 18th century, the English ballad meant more to most people. The love songs in this part of the book are still direct and in touch with their audiences. The lovely terraces of Georgian town houses in London, Bath and York as well as country houses absorbed much music throughout the 18th century and the most popular, by far, were the ballads. Singing teachers flourished and their teaching material was the ballad; English songs, especially love songs, were – as a favourite collection called *The Monthly Melody* testified – 'polite entertainment for ladies and gentlemen'.

Spring Gardens at Vauxhall
1751

According to its inscription, this picture was engraved by E. Rooker in 1751 from a sketch by 'Canaleti' (?Canaletto, who painted many pictures of the Thames and the City of London in the eighteenth century). It shows the Grand Avenue, taken from the entrance with a singer (?Kitty Clive) accompanied by the orchestra in the 'rotunda', flutes and horns on her right, strings and harpsichord (?'Dr' Arne) on her left.

LET NOT LOVE ON ME BESTOW

Richard Steele

Daniel Purcell

Notes The tempo here should be a flowing one-in-a-bar, despite the decorations on 'eager', for the essence of this song is enthusiasm. These two bars are really written-out turns, and therefore should be executed lightly. Careful note must be taken of the placing of the commas to show the subtlety of the phrasing. The repetitions of 'all' can be used to build up the excitement. Original key B♭ major.

I know none, no, no, no, none but sub-
-stan-tial bliss-es, Ea-ger glan-ces,
ea-ger glan-ces, so-lid kiss-es.
I know not what the lo-vers

feign, Of fi - ner plea - sure mixed with
pain. Then pri - thee, pri - thee give me, gen - tle
boy, None of thy grief, but all, all, all,
all, but all, all, all, all, all, all the joy. Pri - thee

give me, pri - thee give me, gen - tle boy,
none of thy grief, but all, all, all, all, but
all, all, all, all, all, all the joy, but
all, all, all, all, all, all the joy.

CELIA THE FAIR

George Monro

Notes This song is well known as 'My lovely Celia' in the arrangement by Lane Wilson. However, he only included two verses, altering the words considerably and writing his own accompaniment. Some suggestions for decoration have been given—others can be applied, and the accompaniment is also open to variation. Be sure to make the most of the sweeping lines of this beautiful, flowing melody.

CUPID, MAKE YOUR VIRGINS TENDER

Daniel Purcell

Notes This is a young man's song, and persuasiveness should be the key-note. The melismas can be used to help point the meaning of the words. The tempo should be a relaxed two-in-a-bar. A slight rallentando in the last two bars will emphasize the final line of the text. Original key A minor.

Such as like a te - - dious woo - ing, Let 'em cru - - - - - - el dam - sels find; But let such as
would, as would be doing, Pri - thee, pri-thee, pri-thee Cu - pid, make 'em kind,
Pri - thee, pri - thee, Cu - pid, make 'em kind.

Thomas Augustine Arne: musical director, Spring Gardens
1710–1778

This etching, after Bartolozzi, shows Arne at a 'continuo' organ (with somewhat elongated keys) playing his most famous song 'Rule Britannia' . . . in full dress with sword. It carries the title 'Harmony and Sentiment' and a verse to be sung to the 'Britannia' tune:

By music minds an equal temper know;
Nor swell too high nor sink too low;
Warriors she fires with animated sands;
Pours balm into the bleeding lovers wounds

O COME, O COME, MY DEAREST

Pritchard

Thomas Arne

Notes This was the only song to survive from the pantomime *The Fall of Phaeton*; it was added to the collection of Shakespeare songs that Arne published in 1741. Sing it with affection, not allowing the decoration to become too heavy.

all the bloom - ing spring, thy lips a - dorned with all the
bloom - ing spring. A thou - sand thou - sand sweets their
tr
Continuo
Violins
fra - grant a - toms blend, Which in a gale of joy, which
tr
Continuo (et sim.)
in a gale of joy thy breath at - tend. Thy
tr

love in gen - tle mur - murs to my soul ap - ply,
Heal me with kiss - es, oh! heal me with kiss - es, or
(Violins colla voce)
else I die, or else I die.
tr

JENNY

Thomas Arne

Notes This is a story, and the words and characters must be clear and pointed. Make the most of the brilliance with which Arne illustrates 'till she sprung from my arms and flew over the plain'. The repeats are authentic but are best omitted.

when she an - gry did say, What's the mean-ing of this? Why these
free-doms, I pray? Dear Jen - ny, I need no a -
(Violins colla voce)
p
- po - lo - gy use, Your charms for my crimes are suf -
tr
- fi - cient ex - cuse, your charms
tr

for my crimes are suf - fi - cient ex - cuse.
1
2
Dear
f Strings
Sure lips sweet as those were for kiss - ing de - creed, sure
p (Violins colla voce)
Strings
lips sweet as those were for kiss - ing de - creed. Cry'd
tr

she, Ve - ry fine, ve - ry pret-ty, in - deed, ve - ry
f p f p f p f p
fine, ve - ry fine, ve - ry pret - ty, in - deed.
f p f
tr
Re - peat - ing this strain then a - gain and a - gain, I

kissed her and press'd her still more to ob - tain, Till she
f p f p
sprung from my arms and flew o - ver the plain, till she
f p f p
sprung from my arms,
she sprung from my arms and flew

o - ver the plain.
original:
Like Daph - ne, she strove my em - brace to e - lude, Like
f
p Continuo
Phoe - bus I quick-en'd my pace and pur-sued, like Phoe - bus I quick-en'd my
p Strings
pace and pur - sued.
What
f
p

Allegretto
fol - low'd, ye lo - vers, must ne - ver be said, what fol - low'd, ye
lo - vers, must ne - ver be said, But 'twas all ve - ry fine, ve - ry
pret-ty in - deed, but 'twas all ve - ry fine, ve - ry pret - ty in -
- deed.

THE FOND APPEAL

Thomas Arne

Notes Plenty of warm, but not sentimental, emotion is needed. Your question is genuine, coming from the heart, and the answer will matter a great deal. This is first love, not flirtation. All the trills can be given turns, whether indicated by Arne or not.

1. Gen - tle youth, O tell me why Tears are start - ing
2. Tell me, when the ap - point - ed hour Calls us to the
3. Tell me, when the pains I feel, Pun - gent as the
p
from my eye When each night from you I part,
sec - ret bower, Blush - ing, trem - bling, why I run
wounds of steel, When I feel the thrill - ing smart,
tr
Why the sigh that rends my heart, why the sigh that
Ear - ly as the ri - sing sun, ear - ly as the
Why I bless the point - ed dart, why I bless the
f
p
tr
rends my heart?
ri - sing sun?
point - ed dart?
Gen - tle youth, O tell me true,

Is it then the same with you? Gen - tle youth, O
tell me true, is it then the same with you?
Is it then the same with you?
tr
f
p
Dal 𝄋

THE TIMELY ADMONITION

Thomas Arne

Notes This moral tale must be presented with a very light touch, and perhaps a certain eye for the gentlemen in the audience. Some ornamentation is desirable, and the tempo is that of a minuet.

(Violins colla voce)
p
1. So sweet was young Da - mon, so gen - tle his look, New plea - sure my fan - cy in - sen - si - bly took, new plea - sure my fan - cy in - sen - si - bly took. His
2. He pressed my hand hard, but it gave me no pain, He kissed and I sighed till he kissed me a - gain, he kissed and I sighed till he kissed me a - gain; Such

3. His hands on my bosom he'd carelessly lay,
And swear all the while he meant nothing but play;
So I let him play on till no more I could bear,
Till then I ne'er dreamt any danger was near.

4. Such toying and playing so stole on my heart,
I found in his transports my bosom took part.
Beware then ye virgins, if Damon appear,
For prudence comes late when your danger's so near.

William Boyce: cathedral organist and composer
1710–1779

This portrait, dated 1776, shows the composer (as he testified in his will made the following year) 'in perfect health'. The painter was J. Russell.

AMOUR SANS SOUCIS

Colley Cibber

William Boyce

Note Always concentrate on the words!

hour she's kind, that hour she's true, And kind is all my
fol - ly to let doubts des - troy What now is re - al
care, and kind is all my care.
bliss, what now is re - al bliss.
Shall I re - sist that
Let your he - ro - ic
kind - ling eye, That looks to me in - clined? Or
sigh - ers quest The game of souls re - fined; My

3. Or if by change, again deceived,
I find the sex untrue,
At least by changing I'm relieved,
And raptures past renew.
Thus, nor the pain, nor anxious care
I feel of higher joy,
But while the wantons wing the air
I shoot them as I fly.

TELL ME NO MORE

?Sir George Etheridge

William Boyce

Notes It appears that the words of this song were the first published work of William Congreve, and were written for a play by Thomas Southerne. The source reads simply 'the words by Mr Congreve', but a pencil comment has been added: 'words actually by Sir George Etheridge in Congreve's *The Maid's Last Prayer*'–this being the title of Southerne's play!

As such I liked, as
You think she's false, I'm
such ca - ressed, She still was con - stant when pos - sessed, She
sure she's kind; I take her bo - dy, you her mind,
could do more for no man, she could do more for
Who has the bet - ter bar - gain? Who, who has the bet - ter
no man.
bar - gain?
Symphony
FINE
2. But oh! her thoughts on
Dal 𝄋

James Hook: child prodigy, organist and composer
1746–1827

This portrait, painted by L. F. Abbott, is undated.

O LISTEN TO THE VOICE OF LOVE

James Hook

tr
1. O
pp
lis - ten, lis - ten to the voice of Love, He
calls my Daph - ne to the grove. The
tr
prim - rose sweet be - decks the field, The
pp
p

2. Where flowers their blooming sweets exhale,
My Daphne, let us fondly stray,
Where whisp'ring Love breathes forth his tale
And shepherds sing their artless lay.
O listen, listen to the voice of Love,
He calls my Daphne to the grove.

3. Come share with me the fruits of spring,
And leave the town's tumultuous noise;
The happy swains all cheerful sing,
And Echo still repeats their joys:
Then listen, listen to the voice of Love,
He calls my Daphne to the grove.

NO, NO, NO, IT MUST NOT BE

James Hook

No, no, no, it must not, must not be, So Phil - lis told me
in the grove. No, no, no, it must not, must not be,
She will not lis - ten, she will not lis - ten
to my love.
tr
tr
tr

FINE
Now spring with
bound - ing steps ad - vance, Scat - t'ring fra - grance through the
air. Now gay, I join the rus - tic dance If the maid I
love was there, if the maid I love was there, if the maid I love was there.
Dal 𝄋 al Fine, poi al 𝄌

Un - cloud - ed skies in - vite the ro - ver, Ev'- ry
shep - herd seeks his fair. I'd en - vy nei - ther
nymph nor swain If the maid I love was there, if the maid I love was
there, if the maid I love was there. No, no,

no, it must not, must not be, So Phil - lis told me
in the grove. No, no, no, it must not, must not
be, She will not lis - ten,
she will not lis - ten to my love. No, no, no, no, it
tr
tr

must not be,
no, no, no, no, it
must not be,
she will not lis - ten,
she will not lis - ten, she will not lis - ten_ to my
tr
love.

TAKE ME, TAKE ME, SOME OF YOU

John Dryden

James Hook

1.Young I am and yet un - skilled How to make a lo - ver yield,
2.Stay not till I learn the way How to fib and how be - tray,
young I am and yet un - skilled how to make a lo - ver yield,
stay not till I learn the way how to fib and how be - tray,
How to keep and how to gain, When to love and when to feign,
E'er I can my thoughts dis-guise, Force a blush or roll my eyes,
rinf.
rinf.
how to keep and how to gain, when to love and when to feign,
e'er I can my thoughts dis-guise, force a blush or roll my eyes,
rinf.
rinf.
p

3. Could I find a blooming youth,
Full of love and full of truth,
Of honest mind and noble mien,
I should long to be sixteen.
Take me, *etc.*

WHEN A TENDER MAID

R.B. Sheridan

Thomas Linley senior

meet his eyes While he un-folds his pain!
bo-som clasp, No mant-ling blush en - sues!
If he takes her hand she
Then to church well pleased the
trem - bles quite!
lov - ers move,
Touch her lips and she swoons out - right! While a
While her smiles her con - tent - ment prove, And a
pit a pat a pit a pat a pit a pit a pat, Her heart a - vows her
pit a pat a pit a pat a pit a pit a pat, Her heart a - vows her
1
2
fright!
love!
fright!
love!

[Dal 𝄋]

HOW MISTAKEN IS THE LOVER

Stephen Storace

Notes This is one of the few arias from the English operas to survive in full score, and that is only because it was originally written for Nancy, with Italian words ('Care donne che bramante'), for use in the opera *Il Re Teodoro in Venezia* by Paisiello; that version was printed in full score. In this English adaptation Storace cut a few bars near the end.

-tent Gives the sem-blance of con - sent. How mis - ta - ken is the
lo - ver Who on words builds hopes of bliss, And fond-ly thinks we love dis -
-co - ver If per - chance we an - swer yes.
ff
[cresc.]
Ah, how vain is art's pro - fes - sion, Tho' the fal-t'ring tongue com - ply;
ff
p.
cresc.

bliss, And fond-ly thinks we love dis - co - ver If per-chance we an - swer
yes. Oft the tongue, the heart be - ly - ing
Dares not ven - ture on de - ny - ing,
oft the tongue the heart be - ly - ing dares not ven-ture on de - ny - ing, But in spite of dis - con -

What a - vails the cold con - fes - sion If th'a-vert - ed eyes de - ny?
Hap-pier far th'ex-pe-rienced swain Knows he tri - umph must at - tain, When in vain suc - cess - less
tri - al Lan-guage gives the faint de - ni - al, the faint de - ni - al, the faint de -
- ni - al: While the eyes be-tray the fic - tion
ff
p
pp

In de - light - ful con - tra - dic - tion,
And the cheeks with blush-es glow and the tongue still fal - ters no, and the
tongue still fal - ters no. How mis - ta - ken is the lo - ver Who on
words builds hopes of bliss, And fond-ly thinks we love dis - co - ver, If per-
mf
p
ff

-chance we an - swer yes, fond - ly, fond - ly thinks we love dis -
mf
- co - ver, if per - chance we an - swer yes, if per -
ff
f
- chance we an - swer yes, if per-chance we an - swer yes, if per-chance we an - swer
p
cresc.
ff
yes.

THE VICTORIAN AND EDWARDIAN DRAWING ROOM

Although 18th-century songs were polite 'entertainment for ladies and gentlemen', composers at Victoria's accession know how to vary their style of writing to reach the widest audience in their ballads and the difference between music for high society and the general public was not very discernible.

Singers in public concerts continued until about the middle of the century to have orchestral accompaniment. Many of their ballads were from stage shows. The publisher then announced the sale of the ballad with piano accompaniment 'as sung by Mr or Madame X' for private performance. The song might then find its way – according to its lyrics and popularity – into a connoisseur's salon (where the guests were invited), any family drawing room or the 'public house' (erstwhile taverns).

Ballads with love lyrics became more sentimental as the century progressed until they often became maudlin in the Edwardian music hall and 'parlour' songs. There were, however, a few English composers throughout this period who could elevate the ballad to the status of artsong after the manner, first, of Haydn then of Schubert, Mendelssohn, Schumann and Brahms. There were also some who cultivated 'national songs' to match the Romantic poets, particularly labelled 'Scottish' and 'Irish' with self-styled 'folk tunes' such as 'Annie Laurie': most of these were collected in Stanford's 'National Song Book' . . . at the recommendation of the Board of Education in their quaintly titled *Blue Book of Suggestions* (1905) for the musical and literary education of 'older children' in schools. The 'airs' masquerading as English folksongs by then included Ford's 'Since first I saw your face' (page 32), Shakespeare/Morley's 'It was a lover' (page 30) and Ben Jonson's 'Drink to me only'; heady stuff for a Victorian teenager.

'New' Romantic poets such as Coleridge and Wordsworth who first published their *Lyrical Ballads* in 1798 were coldly received both by the public and composers. Byron fared better with the public but, apart from love songs such as 'She walks in Beauty, like the night' included in a collection of so-called *Hebrew Melodies* (1815) few composers were inspired to set the poems. Keats and Shelley too, were almost ignored. Tennyson's 'Maud' provided Balfe with the lyrics for one of the most lasting of popular English love songs, widely imitated, often parodied, but now heard again for its simple power when sung 'straight'.

Thomas Attwood turned back to the 17th-century Royalist leader Edmund Waller's most beautiful poem 'Go, lovely Rose!' to which a Cambridge undergraduate Henry Kirke White had added a third verse at the turn of the 19th century. The music is called a 'canzonet' after the success of Haydn's canzonets written in London in the 1790s. Attwood had learnt from Mozart, with the Storaces, in Vienna; he became organist of St Paul's Cathedral and to George IV at Brighton; at Queen Victoria's accession he was organist of the Chapel Royal but he died before her Coronation. Songwriting was a sideline but 'Go lovely Rose!' was a winner, chosen for a monthly selection in the *Musical Library* series in 1835 – the equivalent of a 'Book Club Choice' in today's literary world.

Arne and Hook had kept Shakespeare alive in 18th-century song and the Victorians continued to revere the national bard in new versions of the most popular plays. A typical mixture was *The Comedy of Errors*, made into an 'opera' for Covent Garden in 1819. Though said to be 'selected entirely from Shakespeare' the famous song 'Come live with me' was versified by the librettist from lines of Marlow, lines of Shakespeare and – in verse 2 – his own imagination; Bishop's setting became popular even though the poem was a disaster. In 1830 Henry Bishop succeeded James Hook as Director of Music at the Vauxhall Gardens which, no doubt, accounted for the continued popularity of his earlier songs. As with his predecessor he was dependent on his resident singers and, for Bishop, the rising star was the young Sims Reeves, who later became the greatest of all Victorian tenors.

Another Shakespeare 'casualty' was 'Take, O take those lips away' from *Measure for Measure*. Bishop set the one verse that appears in the Shakespeare folio (with a couple of alternative words); Pierson gave his setting the title 'Love and Grief' and set both verses as they appeared in John Fletcher's *The Bloody Brother* in 1639, following John Wilson's setting (page 42). Perhaps Bishop, despite his reputation as a reprobate, had an eye on his public in the Gardens and did not wish to risk offence.

Pierson is now recognised as 'the English Schumann', but he was fiercely attacked by London critics throughout his life. Henry Hugh Pierson studied in Leipzig where his friends included Mendelssohn and Schumann; he succeeded the newly-knighted Sir Henry Bishop as Professor of Music in Edinburgh in 1833 but later the same year returned to Germany where, as an 'immigrant' he became the 'German composer' Heinrich Hugo Pierson. 'Love and grief', published in Leipzig as one of a collection of Liebeslieder in 1842 shows how 'advanced' a composer Pierson must have seemed to Victorian ears not yet accustomed even to the music of Mendelssohn.

J. L. Hatton's most famous song 'To Anthea' was in print from 1851 to 1892, included in many collections including *The Songs of England* which claimed in 1892 to have in it 'the most popular traditional ditties and the principal songs and ballads of the last three centuries'. The words are faithful to Herrick's original, though the review in *The Athenaeum* of the first edition in 1851 said the harmony was 'more foreign' than many of Hatton's other songs.

In 1851 the Great Exhibition opened in Crystal Palace. With the arrival of a

German bandmaster as director of music in 1855, there began the Saturday concerts which were to last until 1907, to become the new 'première' venue for all English composers. As a matter of deliberate planning for a wide public, every concert, with full orchestra, included four songs and it was not thought in any way odd if the songs were occasionally accompanied by piano only. Among the composers who owed most to the Crystal Palace Concerts were Sterndale Bennett, Parry and Stanford.

By the 1850s, Sims Reeves was at his height, joined for the decade by Madame Clara Novello. Together, and singly, they were engaged to sing at the opening of many 'Town Halls' built in the new middle-class affluence of the 1850s and they were Crystal Palace favourites. 'Indian Love' was sung by Clara Novello at a concert under the composer's direction. Bennett was another *alumnus* of Leipzig; he was even offered a series of concerts at the Gewandhaus (Mendelssohn's creation) in 1853 but was too busy in England. He was thought to have been totally under Mendelssohn's influence as a composer and his lack of interest in 'new' music, coupled with a teaching life crowned by his appointment as Principal of the Royal Academy of Music (1868) and knighthood (1871) may well have prevented 'England's Mendelssohn' from contributing more to the international repertory of solo song. 'Indian Love' is one of only 21 songs Sterndale Bennett is known to have written; unlike Attwood, under whom he sang at St Paul's, Bennett did not have a commercial sense.

The German translator, Klingemann, was a diplomat in London who first introduced Mendelssohn to Scotland (and to Clara Novello) and was his staunch friend for life; the undistinguished lyrics of 'Indian Love' were by a London solicitor friend of Dickens, Lamb, Hazlitt and Leigh Hunt.

Hubert Parry had composition lessons from Sterndale Bennett and – for one long vacation in Germany – Pierson. This jovial old Etonian led England's musical establishment for almost 40 years. Oxford Professor of Music, Director of the Royal College of Music, a knight of Queen Victoria and a baronet of Edward VII. He lived on through the First World War, the most honoured of English composers. Today he is still sung by thousands at the last night of the Summer Promenade Concerts in London – heirs to the Crystal Palace tradition – when they give forth Blake's 'Jerusalem', written when he was approaching 70. Unlike Bennett, who seemed weighed down by the burden of various offices and teaching, Parry never stopped writing with remarkable outbursts of passion such as the setting of Rossetti's 'My heart is like a singing bird'. To be sung, as he wrote, 'joyously', it is one of the most heartening settings of unpromising words ('thick-set', 'paddles in a purple sea', 'pomegranates'?) in the English language.

Stanford, who studied in Germany, absorbed the music of Schumann and Brahms and became almost the *alter ego* of Parry. Whilst Parry was in Oxford, Stanford reigned in Cambridge. When the Royal College of Music opened in 1883 Stanford became professor of composition; in 1894 Parry became Director of the College and Stanford remained Professor of Music in Cambridge. In 1898 Parry was knighted; in 1901 Stanford was knighted. In 1918 Parry died, in the middle of writing a song; in 1924 Stanford died, having just finished the last dozen of 115 published songs. Both had a wide knowledge of English lyric poetry, Stanford particularly at one with poets of any period. For the last two songs in this section, the Victorian and Edwardian terrace houses received *their* versions of Elizabethan and Jacobean poets, set as freshly and directly as ever, with the rich harmonies of a dying age.

Watercolour
by
Turner
1779–1851

The famous English landscape painter captured the atmosphere of a Victorian drawing room beautifully in this picture, now in Petworth House, Sussex.

GO, LOVELY ROSE

Canzonet

Edmund Waller and Henry Kirke White

Thomas Attwood (1765–1838)

For concert performance a short piano introduction should be improvized.

sweet And fair she seems to be. Tell her, that's
cresc.
dolce
young, and shuns to have her gra - ces spied, That hadst thou sprung In de - serts
dolce
where no men a - bide, Thou must have un - com - mend - ed
died, thou must have un - com - mend - ed died, thou

rall.
a tempo
must have un - com - mend - ed died.
Small is the worth Of beau - ty
from the light re - tir'd;
Bid her come forth, Suf - fer her -
- self to be ad - mir'd,
de - sir'd,
And not blush so to
8
8

be ad - mir'd. Then die, that she The com - mon fate of all things rare May
read in thee; How small a part of time they
share, That are so won - d'rous sweet and
fair, that are so won - d'rous sweet and fair, that

rall.
are so won - d'rous sweet and fair.
a tempo
dolce
cresc.
dolce
cresc.
Yet, though thou fade, yet, though thou fade. From thy dead
leaves let frag - rance rise; And teach the

maid That good - ness time's rude hand de - fies; That vir - tue
8
cresc.
lives when beau - ty dies, that vir - tue
p
p
rall.
lives when beau - ty dies.
p
a tempo
poco rit. al fine

Sir Henry Rowley Bishop
1786–1855

This picture of 'The Musical Composer' was presented to the National Portrait Gallery in 1869.

COME LIVE WITH ME

Adapted by Frederick Reynolds from Marlowe and others

Henry Rowley Bishop (1785–1855)

And we will all the plea - sure prove
And we will re - vel, will re - vel all the year
That hills and val - ley, dale and field
In plains and groves, on hills and dales,
And all the crag - gy moun - tains yield.
sostenuto
There will we
Where frag - rant air breathes sweet - est gales.
sostenuto
There shall you

sit up-on the rocks, And see the shepherds feed their flocks,
have the beau-teous pine, The ce - dar, and the spread-ing vine! The
There will I make thee beds of ro - ses, With a thou - sand
birds with heav'n - ly tu - nèd throats, Pos - sess wood
frag - rant po - - - - sies; If these de - lights thy mind may
e - choes, e - choes with sweet notes; If these de - lights thy mind may
pp

Largo
slentando
move, if these de - lights thy mind may move,
slentando
move, if these de - lights thy mind may move,
ad libitum
slentando
a tempo 1mo
Then live with me and be my love, and
pp
mf
p
cresc.
be my love, and be my love, and
f
mf
cresc.
tr
be my love.
f
cresc.
ff
sosten.

TAKE, O TAKE THOSE LIPS AWAY

Shakespeare

Henry Rowley Bishop (1786–1855)

Take, O take those lips a - - way, That so sweet - ly, that so sweet - ly are for - sworn.
were
pp
tr
più f
And those eyes, the break of day, and those eyes, the break of day, Lights which do mis - lead the morn. But my
that
più p espress.
mf
pp
tr
dolce ed espressivo

kisses bring a - gain, but my kisses bring a - gain, Seals of
love, seals of love, seals of love, tho' seal'd in
but
p
vain. And those eyes, the break of day, and those eyes, the break of
f
pp dolce
mf
pp
day, Lights which do mis - lead the morn. But my
ad lib.
tr
3

kiss - es
bring a - gain,
but my kiss - es
bring a -
- gain,
Seals
of love,
seals
of love,
seals of
love, tho'
but
seal'd
in
colla voce
p
vain.
f
tr

COME INTO THE GARDEN, MAUD

Cavatina

WORDS BY
LORD TENNYSON

MUSIC BY
MICHAEL WILLIAM BALFE

done, In gloss of sa - tin and glim - mer of pearls, Queen
li - ly and rose in one; Shine out, lit - tle head, run - ning sun - ning
rall.
o - ver with curls, To the flo - wers, and be their sun. Shine out, shine out, and
riten. a piacere
f
be their sun. Come in - to the gar - den, Maud, For the black bat, night, is has
a tempo
stacc.
pp
flown, Come in - to the gar - den, Maud, She is com - ing, my own, my
p accelerando
rf pp

75
sweet, Were it e - ver so ai - ry a tread, My heart would hear her and
rf p
beat, Were it earth in an earth - y bed;
80 rall.
a tempo, allegro
ff
Come my own, my sweet, come my own, my sweet,
85
Maud, Maud, come, I'm here at the gate a -
pp
cresc.
f
90 a tempo
-lone.

rall.
a tempo
riten. a piacere
here at the gate a - lone. And the wood - bine spi - ces are waft - ed a - broad, And the
colla parte
20
musk of the ro - ses blown; For a breeze of mor - ning moves, And the
rose is
25
pla - net of love is on high, Be - gin - ning to faint in the light that she loves On a
rall.
30
cresc.
riten. a piacere
bed of daf - fo - dil sky, To faint in the light of the sun she loves, To
cresc.
a piacere
35
faint in the light and to die. Come! Come!
his

★ If it is desired to use Tennyson's text in performance, the word 'Queen' should be sung to a quaver D.

LOVE AND GRIEF

(*Lieb und Leid*)

WORDS ATTRIBUTED TO
JOHN FLETCHER
partly after William Shakespeare
German translation partly by
A. W. von Schlegel and L. Tieck

MUSIC BY
HENRY HUGO PIERSON

15 appassionato
But my kiss-es bring a-gain, Seals of love, though sealed in vain, though sealed in vain,
Doch den Kuss gieb mir zu-rück, fal - sches Sie - gel, fal - sches Sie gel fal schem Glück,
appassionato
seals of love, though sealed in vain, though sealed in vain, sealed in vain!
fal - sches Sie - gel, fal-sches Sie - gel fal-schem Glück, fal - schem Glück!
sf
20
calando
p calando
a tempo
25
2. Hide, oh hide those hills of snow
2. Birg der schnee'-gen Hü - gel Pracht,
Which thy fro - zen bo - som bears,
drun-ter fro - stig pocht dein Herz,
On whose
drauf ein

30
tops the pinks that grow Are of those that Ap - - ril wears;
Knos-pen-fä - cher lacht lieb-lich wie die Blüth' im März;
leggiero
mf
appassionato
But first set my poor heart free, Bound in i - cy
Sieh dies ar-me Herz, be-freis aus den Fes - seln,
appassionato
35
sf
rit.
chains, in i - cy chains by thee, bound in i - cy chains by thee, by
aus den Fes-seln starr wie Eis, sieh dies ar - me Herz, be-freis, be-
f
p
Ped.
40
thee!
-freis!
a tempo, ma con anima
sf

TO ANTHEA, WHO MAY COMMAND HIM ANYTHING

Robert Herrick

John Liptrot Hatton (1809–1886)

Allegro

VOICE

PIANO

ff

Bid me to live, and I will live Thy

5

Pro - tes - tant to be: Or bid me love, and

dim.

p

I will give A lov - ing heart to thee. A

10
heart as soft, a heart as kind, A heart as sound and free, As
15
in the whole world thou canst find, That heart Ile give to thee.
dim.
mf
20
Bid
dim.
p
that heart stay, and it will stay, To ho - nour thy De - cree: Or
25
cresc.
f
p

bid it lan - guish quite a - way, And't shall doe so for thee. Bid
sosten.
sempre p
30
me to weep, and I will weep, While I have eyes to see: And
hav - ing none, yet I will keep A heart to weep for thee. Bid
35
dim.
p
con espress.
me des - paire, and Ile des - paire, Un - der that Cy - presse tree: Or
40

45
bid me die, and I will dare E'en Death, to die for thee. Thou
p
f
sempre f
8
art my life, my love, my heart, The ve - ry eyes of
cresc.
molto
50
con passione
me: And has com - mand of ev - 'ry part, To
ff
55
live and die for thee.
colla voce
ff
Ped.
*

INDIAN LOVE

(Indische Liebe)

Barry Cornwall
German translation by C. Klingemann

William Sterndale Bennett (1816–1875)

Slowly

VOICE

PIANO

lento **p**

p

Tell me not that thou dost love me, Though it thrill me with de-light; Thou art like the stars a-bove me, I the low-ly earth at night, the low-ly earth at

Darfst mir Lie-be nicht ge-lo-ben, ob's mit Won-ne mich er-füllt, du bist wie der Stern da dro-ben, Ich die Erd' in Nacht ge-hüllt, die Erd' in Nacht ge-

5 10

dim. **p**

15
night.
-hüllt.
20
Hast thou,(thou from kings de - scend - ed,) Lov'd the In - dian cot-tage born;
Hast du, Held vom Kö - nigs - stam - me, mich die nie - dre Magd ge - liebt,
25
And shall she whom love be - friend - ed, Dark - en all thy hope - ful morn,
und zum Lohn der heh - ren Flam - me wür - de nun dein Pfad ge-trübt!
dim.
30
dark - en all thy hope - ful morn?
wür - de nun dein Pfad ge - trübt!

(With emphasis)
35
Go! and for thy fa - ther's glo - ry,
Auf! dem Ruh - me stol - zer Ah - nen
Wed the blood that's pure and free,
bring dein Blut so frei und rein,
p
'Tis enough to gild my sto - ry,
schei - den auch sich un - sre Bah - nen,
p
40
cresc.
That I once, that I once,
fühl ich doch, fühl ich doch,
p
pp
I once was loved by
du wa - rest, wa - rest
45
thee!
mein!
smorzando

Sir Hubert Parry, Bt.
1848–1918

Percy Scholes, compiler of the *Oxford Companion to Music*, was one of Parry's last pupils in Oxford. Recalling his tutor in 1938, 'Parry was everything that one would like the world to consider as implied in the description "English gentleman".' This photograph was taken c. 1890.

MY HEART IS LIKE A SINGING BIRD

Christina Rossetti

Hubert Parry

cresc.
heart is like an ap - - ple - tree Whose
cresc.
boughs are bent with thick - set fruit; My
p
p
heart is like a rain - bow shell That
pad - dles in a pur - ple sea; My heart is glad-der than
hal - cyon
f
f

slower, dolce
p
all these Be - cause my love is come to
slower
p
a tempo
me.
a tempo
cresc.
f
dim.
mf
Raise me a da - is of pur - ple and gold;
silk and down;
mf
cresc.
Hang it with vair and pur - ple dyes;

p
mf
Carve it in doves and pome - gra - nates, And
p
cresc. ed animando
pea - - - cocks with a hun - - dred eyes;
mf cresc. ed animando
cresc. sempre
Work it in gold and sil - ver grapes, In
3
cresc. sempre
poco allargando
a tempo
f
leaves and sil - - ver fleur - de-lys; Be -
poco allargando
a tempo
f

-cause the birth-day of my life Is come,
my love is come to
me.
mf
f
mf
f
3

Sir Charles Villiers Stanford.
1852–1924
Drawn by
William Rothenstein

THE MERRY MONTH OF MAY

Thomas Dekker

C.V. Stanford

mf
O and then did I un - to my true love say,
Sweet Peg, sweet
Peg, sweet Peg,
thou shalt be
my Sum-mer's, Sum - mer's Queen.
mf
mp
Now the
Night - in - gale, the pret-ty Night-in-gale, The sweet - est sing-er, the sweet - est sing-er in

all the Fo - rest quire. En - treats thee sweet Peg - gy, to
hear thy true love's tale, Lo, yon-der she sit - teth, yon-der she sit - teth, her
breast a - gainst a brier.
O the month of May, the mer - ry month of May, So
mf
mp
p

fro - lic, so gay, so fro - lic, so gay and so green, so green, so green:
O and then did I un - to my true love say,
mf
Sweet Peg, sweet
Peg, sweet Peg,
thou shalt be my Sum - mer's,
Sum - mer's Queen.

O MISTRESS MINE

Shakespeare

C.V. Stanford

cresc.
sweet - ing; Jour-neys end in lo - vers' meet - ing,
cresc.
f
Ev - 'ry wise man's son doth know.
f
mf
mp
What is love? 'Tis not here -
p
f
-af - ter; Pre - sent mirth hath pre - sent laugh - ter; What's to
p
cresc.
p

cresc.
come is still un - sure:
In de -
cresc.
- lay there lies no plen - ty;
Then come kiss me,
f
sf
sweet-and-twen - ty,
Youth's a stuff will not en -
rall.
mf
rall.
a tempo
- dure.
a tempo
f

Angel with Lute
(Morte d'Arthur)
Pen and ink drawing
by
Aubrey Beardsley
1872–98
Tennyson's *Morte d'Arthur* was published in
1842.

THE RECITAL ROOM

England had no permanent opera company before the First World War and English singers were able to make a career without the 'big' voice, concentrating on musicianship and beauty of tone. It is this quality in the English lyric singer which has become envied throughout the continent in recent years, particularly since the advent of broadcasting. The 'recital' given by one singer in a small public concert hall – such as the Bechstein (now Wigmore) Hall in London – became a feature of English musical life in the early part of the century and is still a regular feature in music clubs, libraries, hotel 'musical' weekends and arts centres, more in England than in most other countries of the world.

To make a recital programme, singers began to offer songs in several languages – German *lieder*, French *mélodies*, Spanish *villancicos* and even Russian and Scandinavian songs. Songs with piano accompaniment became, as the German composer Wolf first called them, 'Songs for voice and piano'. The interest of an independent piano part added to the artistic worth of a song. Composers produced sets of songs – song cycles – for the recital room or hall and gradually, as the 20th century endured the social convulsions of two world wars, love songs became 'art' in the concert world and 'serious' radio . . . the popular expression of love in song passed to the film musical and the 'pop' record industry.

The early days of broadcasting in the 1920s brought an end to demands for public recitals but, since song recitals have remained a regular feature of 'serious' broadcasting, radio has equally provided stimulus for composers to continue to set words to music for solo performance and, disseminated through the record industry, some modern art songs have become popular. The repertoire of most solo singers however, is still that of 100 years ago. This last section may therefore seem valedictory to the story of English Love Songs.

In mild reaction to the 'invented' folksong of the 19th century, several English composers, led by Cecil Sharp and Vaughan Williams, sought through convivial trips into country pubs and carnivals to re-discover *real* folksongs and arrange them for solo recitals and amateur choirs.

Amongst the most gifted was a man who could find nothing to do with his life until the First World War, and then revealed undreamt-of powers of leadership. He was killed in the Battle of the Somme at the age of 31: George Butterworth. An old Etonian, he may well have been thought a dilettante by his fellow composers but in him there survived the sweet lyricism of English song. As early as 1911 he put together a cycle of *11 Folk Songs from Sussex*. The first three are printed here, showing his skill in simple piano writing, in rhythmic flexibility and in expressing the spirit of innocent poetry in an unaffected way. Butterworth had a guileless taste.

Peter Warlock, on the other hand, had considerable guile in his 'folky' songs and may well have become a successful politician or civil servant. But there is no doubt of his passion for music and his admiration of the one composer who shaped his whole life: Frederick Delius. The reader and listener is invited to compare 'The Droll Lover' with Butterworth's 'A blacksmith courted me' in the treatment of folk-like melody and then turn from 'The Contented Lover' to Delius's 'Longing' to hear how all belong to the mainstream of English love songs.

Despite his Leipzig training and setting Norwegian and Danish poets, Delius retained an English directness in his songwriting: the translations, which are in the composer's manuscript, must be understood with the same tolerance as we now accord Tennyson. This was the lyric language of the time and Delius (who, after all, also set Tennyson's 'Maud' cycle) felt the words deeply enough in his rich, post-Wolf, harmonies.

The Stanford and Parry style is still evident in Butterworth's 'I fear thy kisses' – one of the few successful settings of Shelley. John Ireland strains the style to its limit in the very fulsome setting of 'My true love hath my heart', uncovering a more complex passion than Sir Philip Sidney, maybe, intended – a pupil of Stanford, Ireland wrote 15 song cycles in addition to the selection of individual songs chosen here. His choice of poets was always interesting; his piano writing is that of a good pianist and needs a sensitive ear not to stifle his fragile melodic gifts.

Frank Bridge was considered what we would now call an 'avant-garde' composer by young composers at the end of the 20s – Britten and Walton amongst them. He had studied with Stanford, but the bitterness the First World War left on his belief in peace, led him into his own, more private view of love in the world. The Indian poet Tagore's sense of beauty drew him into the strange, still sound world of 'Speak to me, my love'. The dedication of 'Dweller in my deathless dreams' may seem surprising. The Irish Count John McCormack was the most fashionable tenor of his day, known for his Irish ballads, and this was not his usual poetic territory. As has happened so often in the history of English song, the singer inspired the composer as much as the poet.

So it was with Gustav Holst, for whom Dorothy Silk was the ideal soprano. In the last song he ever wrote, to the words of the 'Civil Service poet' Humbert Wolfe (then an officer in the Ministry of Labour), the sound of the voice he had in his ears could well have inspired the exquisite ending 'You cannot dream things lovelier'.

Last in this tribute to the long line of lyrical English songwriters is the unsung Edmund Rubbra, who may well one day be recognised as the 20th-century Dowland in his affinity with English verse. Now (1980) in his eightieth year, his settings of two Spenser sonnets take us back to the first great love poet of the English language, exultant at the joy of love in the Spring of life:

> Make haste, therefore, Sweet love, whilst it is prime;
> For none can call again the passed time.

Woodcut
by
Gwen Raverat

Now in the Victoria and Albert Museum.

YONDER STANDS A LOVELY CREATURE

p
4."What care I for gold and sil - ver, What care I for house and land?
5. "Ri - pest ap - ples soon - est rot - ten, Hot - test love it soon gets cold:
6. "Af - ter net - tles then come ro - ses, Af - ter night then in comes day:
p
What care I for the world of plea - sure, So long as I've got a nice young
Young men's words are soon for - got - ten, So pray, young man, don't speak too
Af - ter a false love then a true love, So we - pass our time a -
1, 2
3
man?"
bold!"
- way."
1, 2
3
pp

SOWING THE SEEDS OF LOVE

blos - som in A - pril, in May, and in June, When the
chose me the li - ly, the vio - let and pink, Each of
vio - let and pink I did both o - ver - look, And so
times I've been kissed by those red ro - sy lips, Till I
wish that I was in that young man's arms, That has
1, 2, 3, 4
small birds do sweet - ly sing. 2. My
them I re - fused all three. 3. The
now I must bide till June. 4. In
gained the green wil - low tree. 5. The
sto - len this heart of
1, 2, 3, 4
Last time
mine.
Last time
pp

A BLACKSMITH COURTED ME

ham - mer all in his hand he looked so brave and
fear the scorch - ing suns will shine and spoil his
is no truth in man, nor in fa - ther nor in

dimin.
cle - ver, And if I was with my love, I would
beau - ty, And if I was with my love, I would
bro - ther, And since I have lost my love, I will
dimin.

Last time
live for e - ver.
do my du - ty.
seek no oth - er.
2. My
3. Strange
(tacet)
Last time
p
rit. last time
pp

THE CONTENTED LOVER

James Mabbe

Peter Warlock

wight
Since
she
now
loves
thee
best
Who
is
thy
heart's
de -
light.
Let
joy
be
thy
soul's
guest,
mf
p
Ped.
mf

EYNSFORD. July 1928.

THE DROLL LOVER

Anon XVII century

Peter Warlock

love thee for thy wan - ton - ness, And for thy droll - er - y, For
L.H. R.H.
Ped.
if thou had'st not loved to sport, Then thou had'st ne'er loved me.
mf
I love thee for thy
p
pov - er - ty, And for thy want of coin; For if thou had'st been
mf

EYNSFORD. July 1928.

Delius
1862–1934
Drawing by
Edvard Munch
1863–1944

Known as 'Fritz' to his friends in Germany and Scandinavia Delius was born in Bradford, Yorkshire and christened as 'Frederick'.

LONGING

SEHNSUCHT

Julius Paulsen
English words by W. Grist

F. Delius

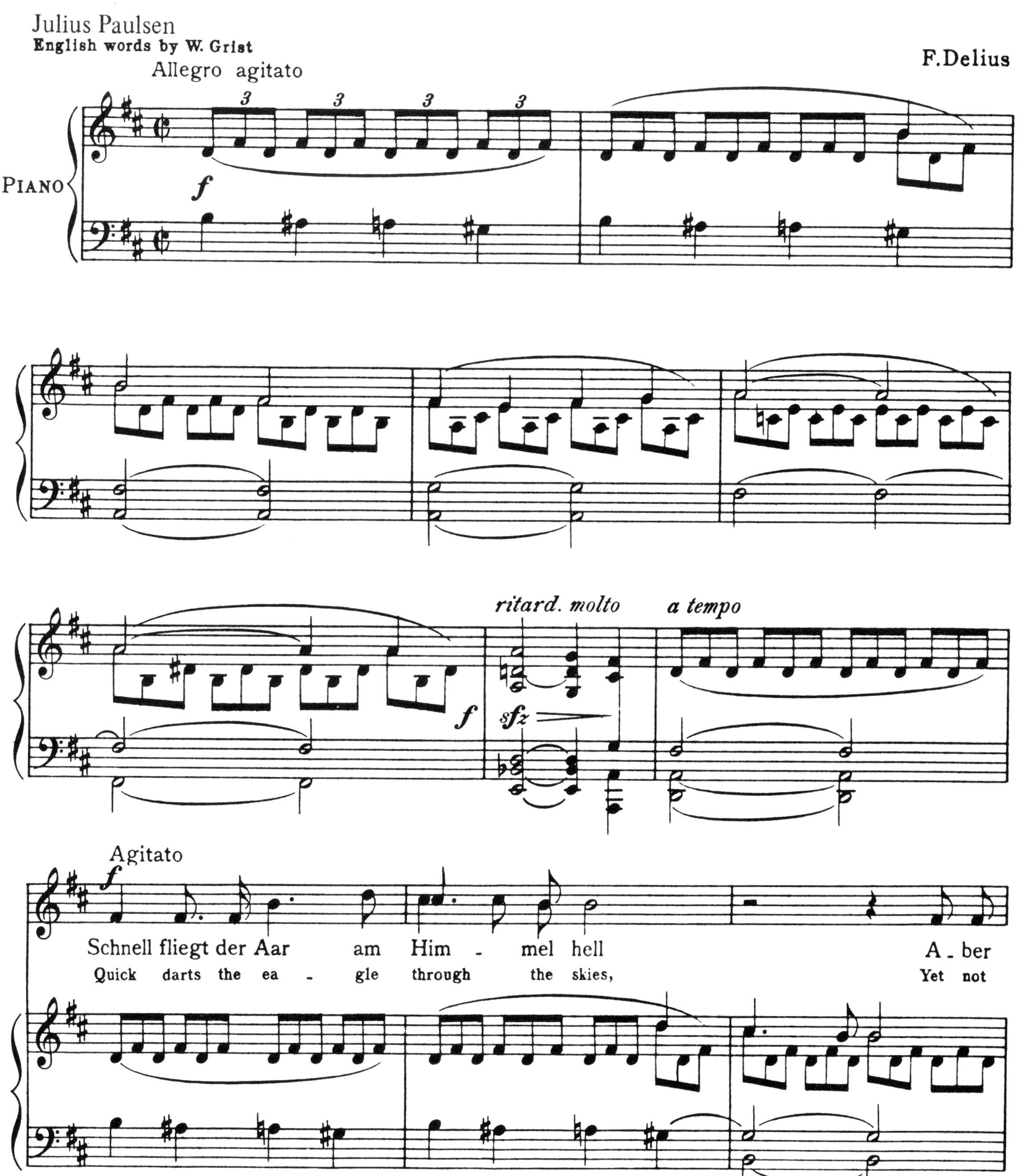

nicht wie die Sehn - sucht schnell;
swift as my long - ing flies;
Zeit, kannst Du denn nicht
Speed on, time! do not
ei- -len? vom A - bend und bis zum Mor - gen - roth,
lan- -guish! From ev - 'ning gray, till the rud - dy morn
da ist's als litt man auf's Neu' den Tod
With mor - tal pangs I'm ev - er torn
den
I'm
rallentando e dimin.
Tod
torn
Lento
Nie kann die Wun - de mir hei - len!
Nev - er al - layed is my an - guish.
sfz

p
cresc. poco a poco
sfz
f
Molto agitato
ff
Es giebt nicht wo die Wo - ge kracht
Where bil - lows thun - der and dash in might,
ff
ff
ben marcato
dim.
Es giebt nicht in des Gra - bes Nacht und
Where tombs are yawn - ing in gloom - y night Where
dim.

Passionato
Meno mosso
ff
giebt, Ach, kei - ne grössʼ - re Qual Als Sehn - sucht,
all re - sist - less reigns the pow - er of long - ing
ff
sfz

als Sehn - - - - - - - - sucht.
of long - - - - - - - - ing
ff
ff

2

Herz, o mein Herze poche nicht so;
Sag, Gedanke, wo weilst du wo?
Traum ist dir gleich den Schwingen!
Das weiss das Glück, das gross und hehr,
Die Qual ist mehr, als Worte leer.
Liebliche Töne mir klingen.
Je grösser das Glück, je grösser die Qual
Wie hoher Felsen und tiefes Thal,
Wie Tag und Nacht so ist mein Sinn.
Ich fühl's, mir brennet tief darin
Die Sehnsucht.

2

Heart, oh! my heart thy throbbing stay
Whither, fancy, thy rapid way.
Dreams but charm thee to vanish.
Her loftiest flight, well fortune knows,
But heralds grief and untold woes
Love only sorrow can banish.
The greater the bliss, the deeper the pain
As lofty hill as lowland plain.
As day and night, as ebb and flow
Within me burns the joy, the woe
Of longing.

THE PAGE SAT IN THE LOFTY TOWER

J. P. Jacobsen

Frederick Delius

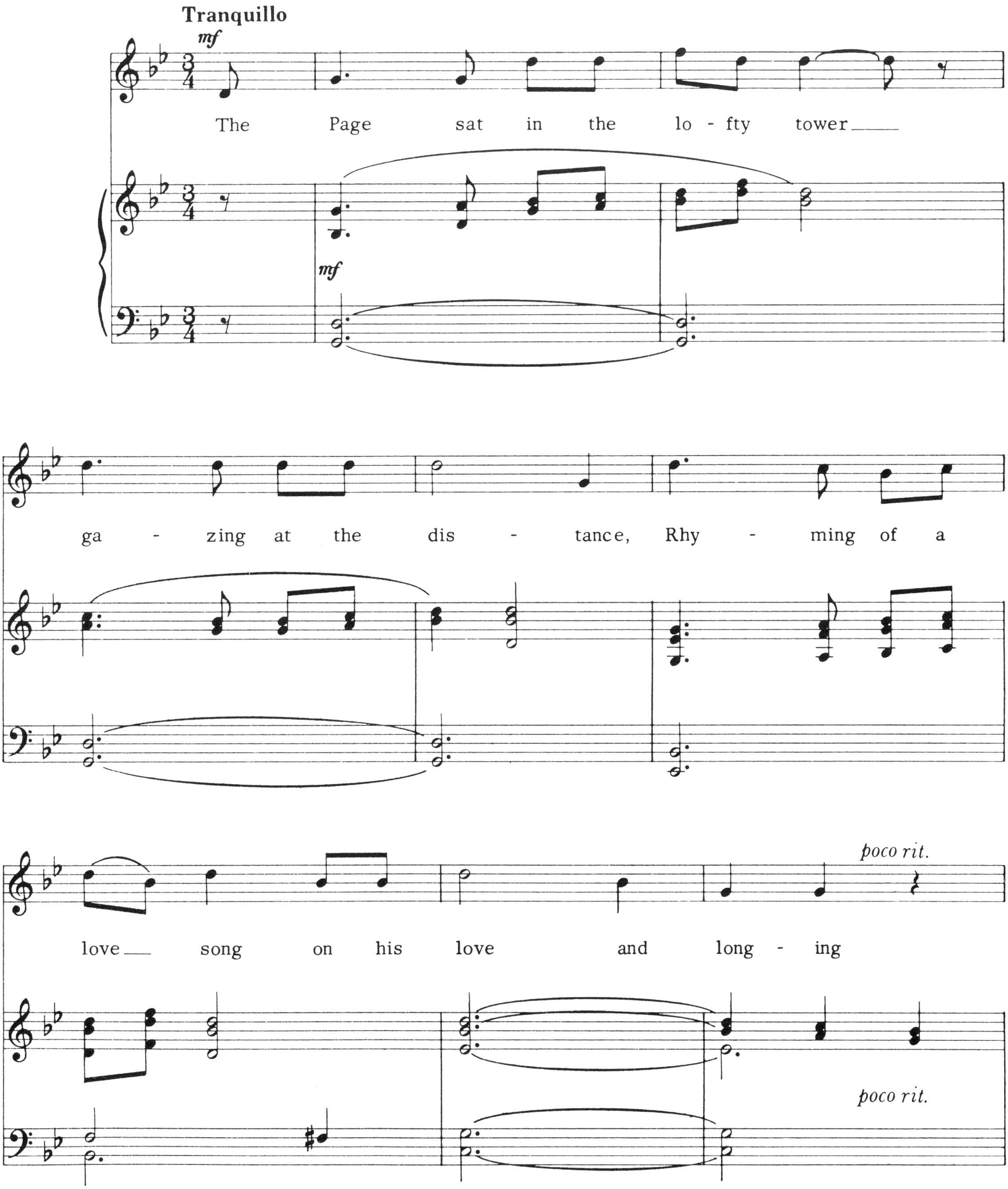
Tranquillo
mf
The Page sat in the lo - fty tower
mf
ga - zing at the dis - tance, Rhy - ming of a
poco rit.
love song on his love and long - ing
poco rit.

So con-fused the words came throng - ing
sfz
Vain his sear - ching.
p
Più vivo
cresc. ed appassionato poco a poco
Now with bright stars Now with ro - ses
No - thing could be rhymed with ro - ses

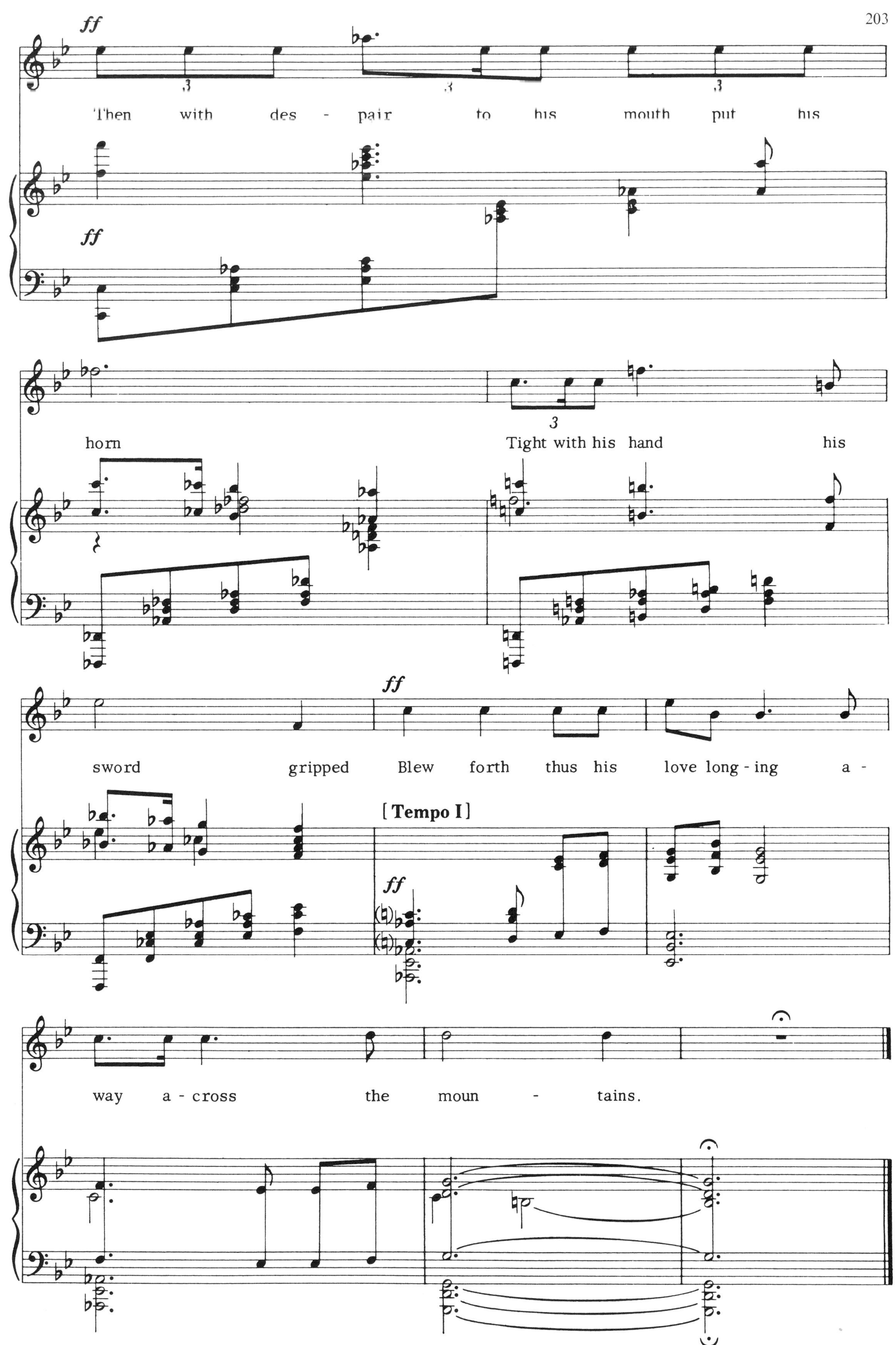
ff
Then with des - pair to his mouth put his
ff
horn
Tight with his hand his
sword gripped
ff
Blew forth thus his love long - ing a -
[Tempo I]
ff
way a - cross the moun - tains.

SUMMER EVE

AM SCHÖNSTEN SOMMERABEND WAR'S

Theodor Kjerulf
English words by W. Grist

F. Delius

2

Ein schlankes Mädchen mit rothem Band
Im gold'nen dicken Geflecht, —
Mit Strickzeug still auf der Hausflur sass,
Die Ziegenheerde am Felsen frass,
Die thät sie hüten
Und Quellen glitten
Gelind durch's Gras.

3

Was träumte sie wohl, die schlanke Maid
Hinaus in die dämmernde Nacht? —
Alleine, einsam ihr wird wohl bang'?
Ob Sehnsucht wohl übern Fels sich schwang
Horch, ferne Lieder!
Rings hallt es wieder
Wie Wehmuthsklang.

2

At housedoor sits a graceful maid,
In ribands golden-bright arrayed,
And as her needle she plies, she heeds
Her flock that o'er the green hill feeds;
Its pathway guiding
To streamlet gliding
O'er grassy mead.

3

Of what dreams she, that maiden fair,
Outgazing through the twilight air?
Though silent, she's not in heart alone,
Her fancy o'er the hill has flown;
Hark, distant singing,
Its echoes winging
In lovelorn tone.

I FEAR THY KISSES

P. B. Shelley

George Butterworth

bur - - - - - - den thine.
p
p
I fear thy
pp
mien, thy tones, thy mo - tion Thou need-est
cresc.
not fear mine

f
In - - - no - cent is the heart's de -
f
vo - - tion With which I wor - - - - -
f
rit.
a tempo
- - - - - ship thine.
p
rit.
a tempo
p
p
(♭)
(♭)
(♮)
(♮)
rit. al fine

John Ireland
1879–1962
Painting by
G. Roddon

An 80th birthday painting of the composer, still showing the human understanding of his songs.

MY TRUE LOVE HATH MY HEART

Sir Philip Sidney

John Ireland

hold his dear, and mine he can - not
miss, There ne - ver was a bet - ter bar - gain
cresc.
driv'n: My true love hath my heart, and I have
f

his.
His heart in me keeps
ff
f
dim.
mp
Ped.
him and me in one, My heart in him his
thoughts and sen - ses guides: He loves my
cresc.
f

heart, for once it was his own, I
mp
cher-ish his be-cause in me it bides: My true
cresc.
(poco animando)
f
love hath my heart, and I have his.
ff
sf
sf

LOVE AND FRIENDSHIP

Emily Brontë

John Ireland

rose - briar blooms,
But which will bloom most con - stant-ly?
mf
The wild rose-briar is
sweet in spring,
mp
Its sum-mer blossoms
scent the air;
cresc.
Yet wait
poco f e marc.

— till win - ter — comes a - gain, ——— And
who will call the wild - briar fair? ———
(♪= ♪)
allarg.
(broad)
cresc.
f marc.
Then, scorn ——— the sil - ly rose-wreath
now, ——— And deck thee with the hol - ly's sheen,
meno f
dim.

That, when De-cem-ber blights thy brow,
He still may leave thy gar-land green, He
still may leave thy gar-land green.
mp
poco f
ten.
poco ten.
a tempo
p
pp

THE TRELLIS

Aldous Huxley *

John Ireland

* Words reprinted from Oxford Poetry, 1918 (Blackwell)

mal - ice And all an - noys,
And we
poco cresc.
lie ros - - - i - ly bow'r'd
mp
cresc.
f
tenuto
ff
dim.
Through the long aft - er - noons And eve - nings
mp

end - less - ly Drawn out, when sum-mer swoons In per-fume
mf
dim.
wind - less-ly, Sounds our light laugh - - - ter,
pp
delicato
p
poco cresc.
With whis-per'd words be -
mf dim.
p
tween And si - lent kiss - es.
pp

January, 1920

IF WE MUST PART

Ernest Dowson

John Ireland

"Un - til to - mor - row or some o - ther day, If we must
part." Words are so weak When
love hath been so strong: Let si - lence speak:
"Life is a lit - tle while, and love is

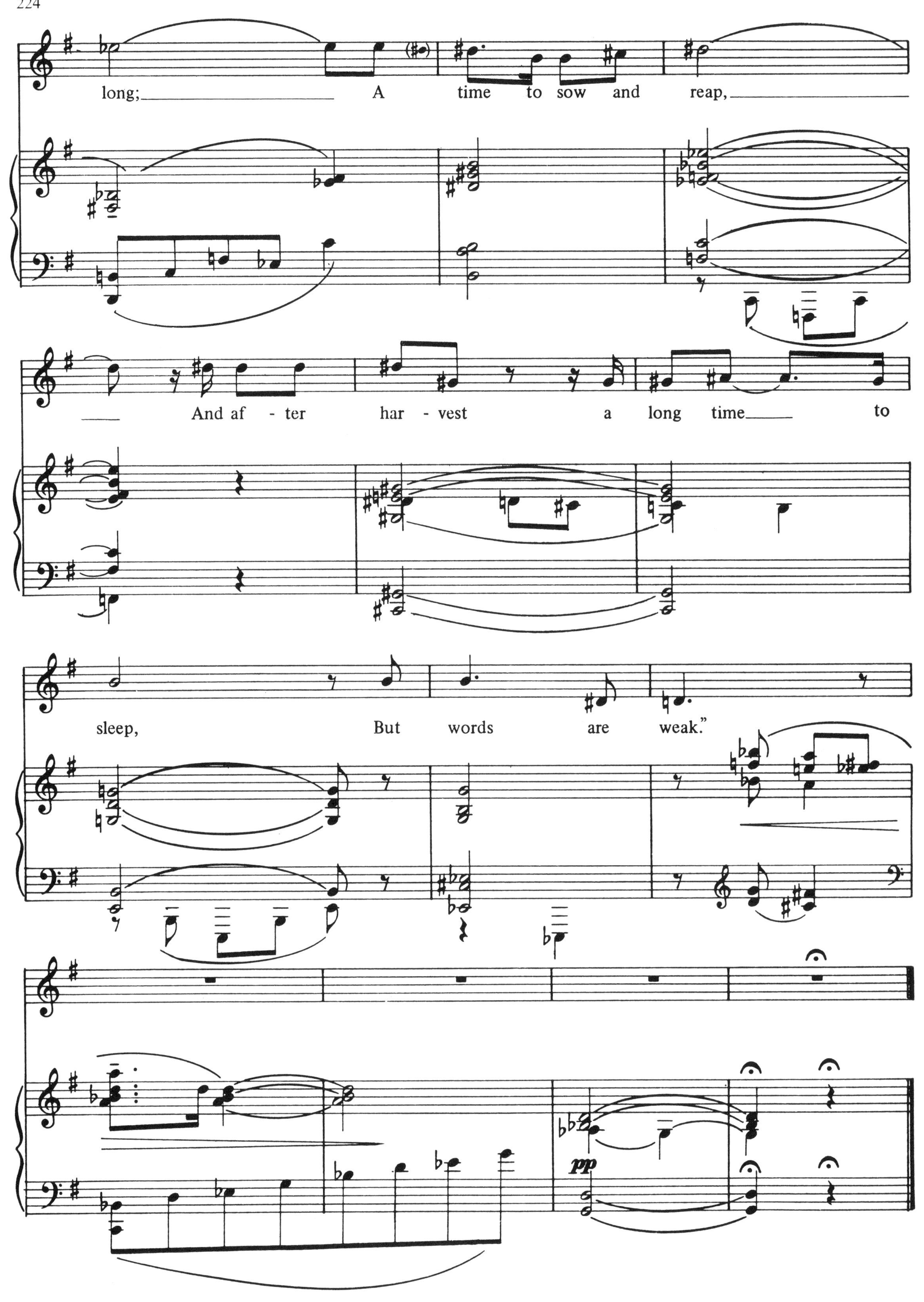
long; A time to sow and reap,
And af - ter har - vest a long time to
sleep, But words are weak."
pp

SPEAK TO ME, MY LOVE!

Rabindranath Tagore

Frank Bridge

p sotto voce
The night is
pp espress.
dark.
The stars are
lost in clouds.
The wind is sigh - ing through the

p dolcissimo
leaves.
I will let loose my hair.
p
pp espress.
My blue cloak will cling round me like night. I will clasp your
head to my bo-som; and there in the sweet lone - li - ness
mur - mur on your heart.
I will shut my
cresc.
mf

Poco a poco animato
cresc.
eyes and lis-ten. I will not look in your face.
ppp
p
cresc.
rit.
f rit.
mp
When your
p
Tempo I ma calmato
words are end-ed, we will sit still and si-lent.
p semplice
pp
Allegro con moto
pp
dim.
ppp
Ped.

Meno mosso
p calmato
Tempo I ma tranquillo
On - ly the trees will whis - per in the dark.
pp
p espress.
The night will
pale.
poco a poco con anima
mf
The day will
cresc.
mf
cresc.
dawn.
We shall

f molto appass.
look at each other's eyes and
go on our dif - ferent paths.
p cresc.
ff
Allegro animato
Speak,
f allarg.
accel.
f
Moderato
Speak
to me, my
fz

(October 1924)

For John Mc Cormack

DWELLER IN MY DEATHLESS DREAMS

Rabindranath Tagore

Frank Bridge

mf
I
mp
p
mp
paint you and fash - ion you e - - - ver with my
mf
love long - - - ings.
espress.
rit.
a tempo
p espress.
You
a tempo
rit.
pp

a piacere
are my own, my own,
Dwell - er in my
end - - - - less dreams!
rit.
a tempo
pp
rit.
a tempo
pp
rit.
a tempo
mf
Your feet are
a tempo
rit.
mf
ro - sy red with the glow of my heart's de-
cresc.
cresc.

sire,
f
fz appass.
f appass.
Glean - er of my sun - - - - - set
songs!
rit.
rit.
f
dim.
a tempo mf dolce
Your lips are bit - - - - - ter
a tempo
mf
dim.
p

p
cresc.
sweet with the taste of my wine of
cresc.
mf
f appass.
pain.
f agitato
dim.
rit.
a tempo
p
a piacere
You are my own, my
p calmato
own, Dwell - er in my lone - - - - some
rit.
pp
rit.

a tempo
poco rit.
dreams!
a tempo
pp
ppp
poco rit.
Tempo I
pp
With the sha - dow of my
pass - ion have I dark - ened your eyes,
Haunt - er of the
depths of my gaze!
mp

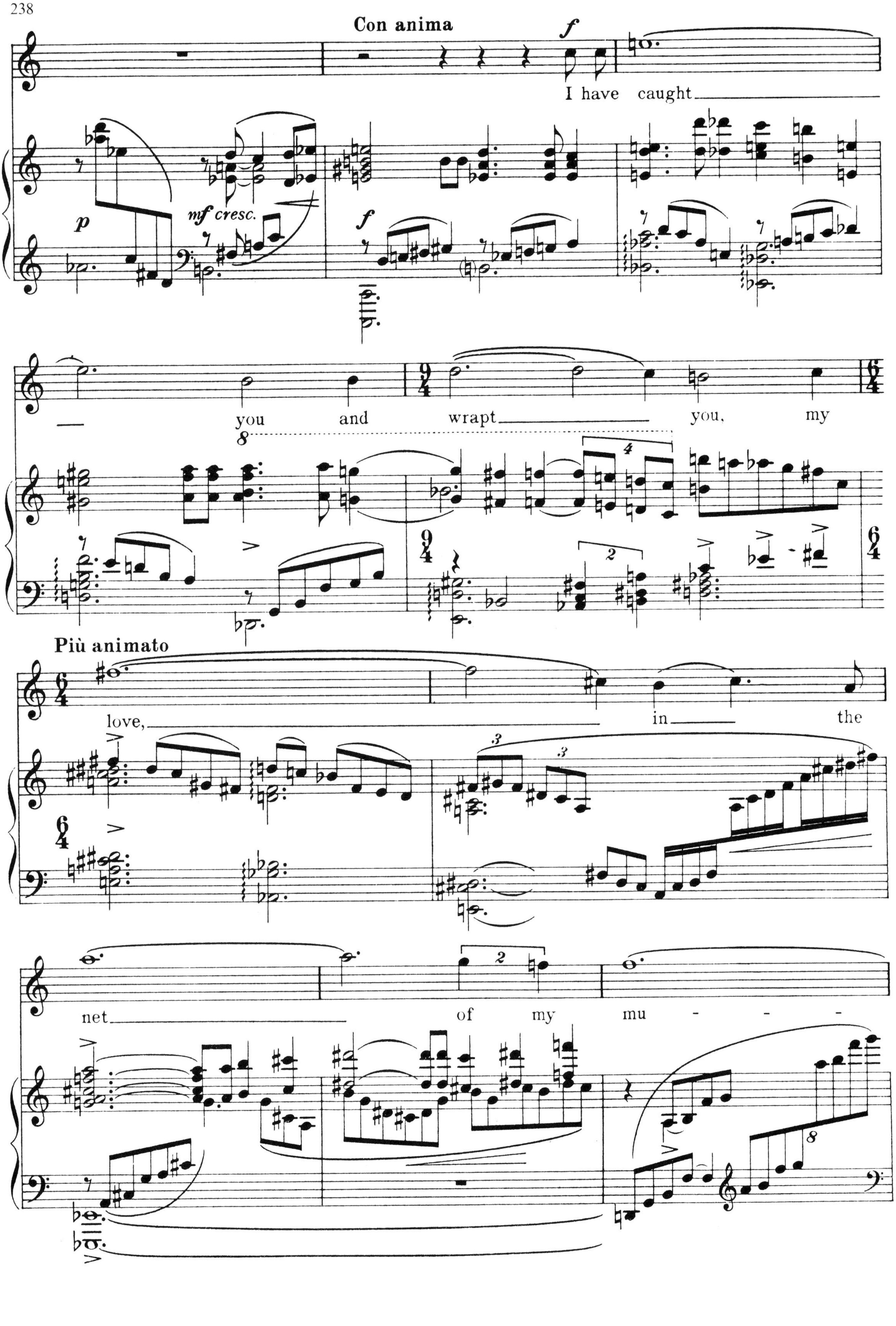
Con anima
f
I have caught
p
mf cresc.
f
you and wrapt you, my
8
4
2
Più animato
love, in the
3
net of my mu - - -
2
8

- - sic.
fz
8
dim. e rit.
fz
Tempo I
mf espress.
You are my own, my own,
8
mp
Ped.
p
pp molto tranquillo
Dwell-er in my death - less dreams!
pp
rit.
8
ppp
perdendosi
Ped. al fine

Gustav Holst
1874–1934
Painting by
Millicent Woodforde
The composer, shown at his working desk, was 36 years old at the time of the painting.

THINGS LOVELIER

Humbert Wolfe

Gustav Holst

THE THOUGHT

Humbert Wolfe

Gustav Holst

hands, because the bones of my hands on yours would press, and you'd say aft - er
f
"Mor - tal was, and crumb - ling, that lov - er's ten - der - ness."
dim.
f
mf
p
Poco meno mosso
p
But I will hold you in a thought with-out mov-ing spi - rit or de-sire or
p
will_ for I know no oth-er way of lov - ing, that en - dures when the heart is still.

A LITTLE MUSIC

Humbert Wolfe

Gustav Holst

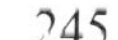

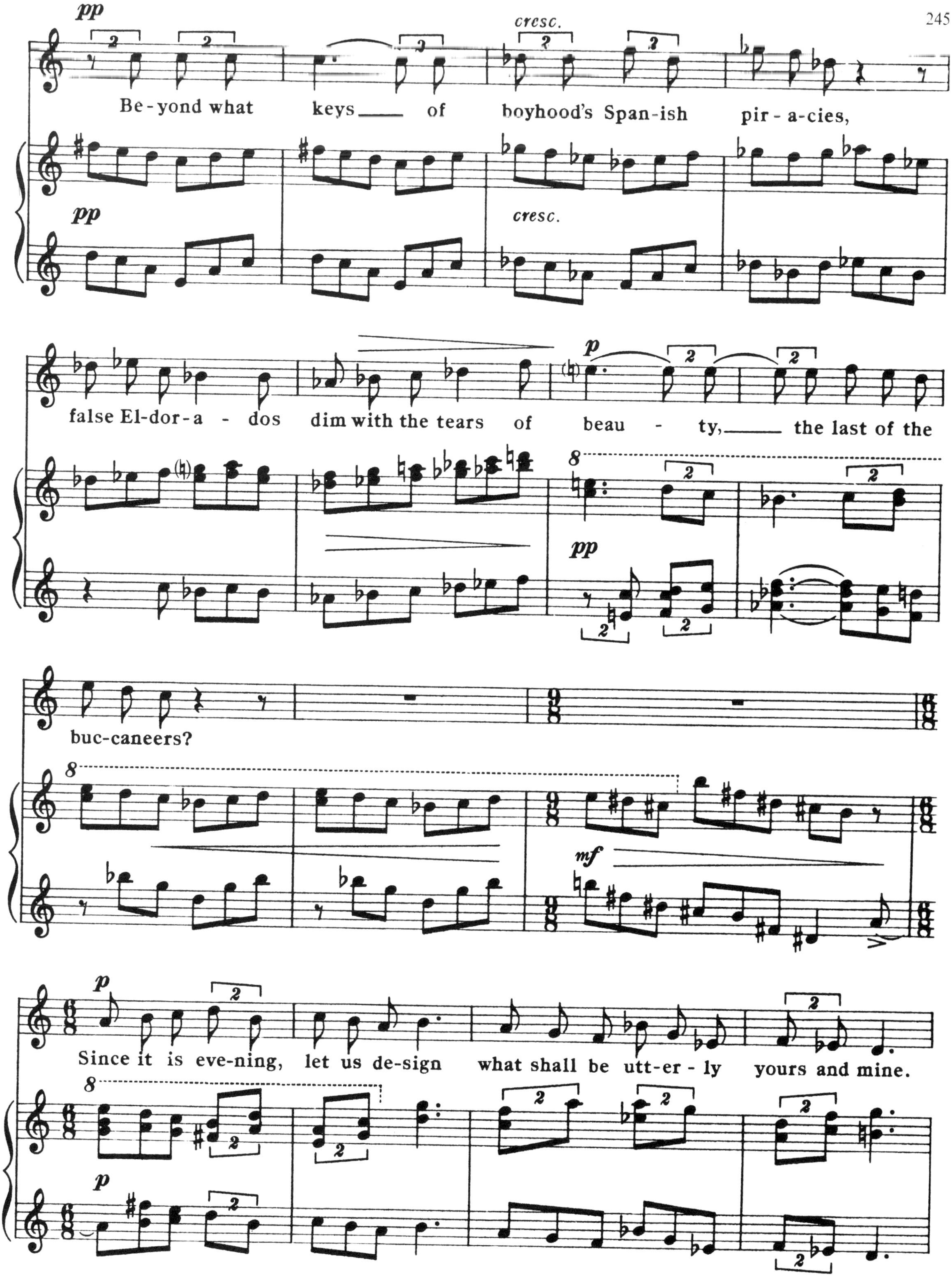
pp
cresc.
Be-yond what keys of boyhood's Span-ish pir-a-cies,
pp
cresc.
p
false El-dor-a-dos dim with the tears of beau-ty, the last of the
8
pp
buc-caneers?
8
mf
p
Since it is eve-ning, let us de-sign what shall be utt-er-ly yours and mine.
8
p

There will be noth-ing that e-ver be-fore beckoned the sail or from an-y
shore.
Poco meno mosso
Trees shall be greener by mountains more pale,
thrush-es out-sing-ing the night-in-gale,
flow-ers now but-ter-flies,
now in the grass,
sud-den-ly qui-et as paint-ed glass, and

Meno mosso
fish-es of em-er-ald dive for the moon, whose sil-ver is stained by the
pea-cock la-goon.
Tempo I
pp
Since it is eve-ning, and
pp una corda
sail-ing wea-ther, let us set out for the dream to-geth-er;
rall.
cresc.
set for the
tre corde
cresc.
rall.
Adagio
dim.
land fall, where love and verse en - fran-chise for e-ver the trav - ell-ers.
dim.

Edmund Spenser
?1552–1599
by an
unknown painter

SONNET XL

Edmund Spenser

Edmund Rubbra

Moderato grazioso

mp

VOICE

PIANO

p

Mark when she smiles with a - mi-a-ble cheare, And tell — me where - to can ye ly - ken it; — When on each eye - lid sweet - ly doe ap-peare An hun - dred Gra - ces as in shade to sit. ————

rit.

dim.

p

Ly - kest it see-meth, in my sim-ple wit, Un - to the fayre sun-shine in so - mers day;

allarg.
That, when a dread-full storme a-way is flit, Thrugh the broad world doth spred his goodly
cresc.
allarg.
a tempo
ray;
f a tempo
marc.
At sight where-of, each bird that sits on spray, And
e - very beast that to his den was fled, Comes forth a-fresh out
marc.
marc.

rall.
a tempo
of their late dis-may, And to the light lift up theyr drouping hed.
rall.
a tempo
mp
p
So
my storme beaten hart like-wise is cheared With that sun - shine,
f
allarg. al fine
allarg. al fine
when cloud-y looks are cleared.
marc.
[f]

(1935)

SONNET LXX

Edmund Spenser

Edmund Rubbra

p
Goe to my love, where — she is care - lesse layd, Yet — in her win - ters bowre not — well a - wake; —
mf
f allarg.
Tell her — the joy - ous time wil not be staid,
f
p
mf
allarg.
f
3

rall. - - - molto
a tempo
Un-lesse she doe him by the fore-lock take;
rall. - - - molto
a tempo
mf
f
Bid her there-fore her-selfe soone
L.H. f
rea-dy make,
To wayt on Love a-mongst his
love - ly crew;
leggiero
Where ev'-ry one, that mis - seth

then her make, Shall be by him a - mearst in pe - nance dew.
L.H.
Make hast, there-fore, Sweet love, whi - lest it is prime; For
aperto
[f]
none can call a - gaine the pas - sed time.
cresc.
allarg.

INDEX OF POETS AND TRANSLATORS

Printed in Great Britain by Galliard (Printers) Ltd, Great Yarmouth